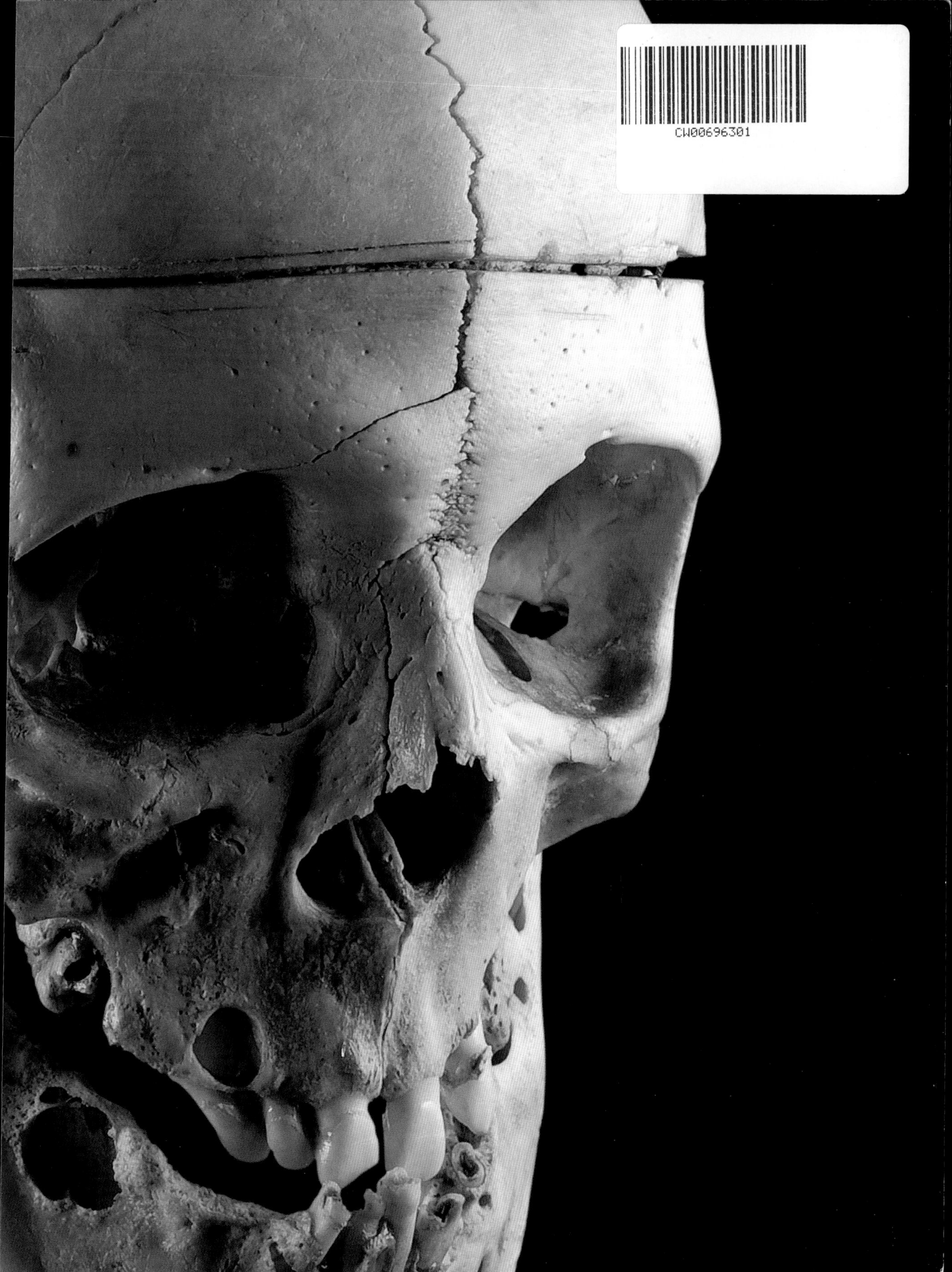
CW00696301

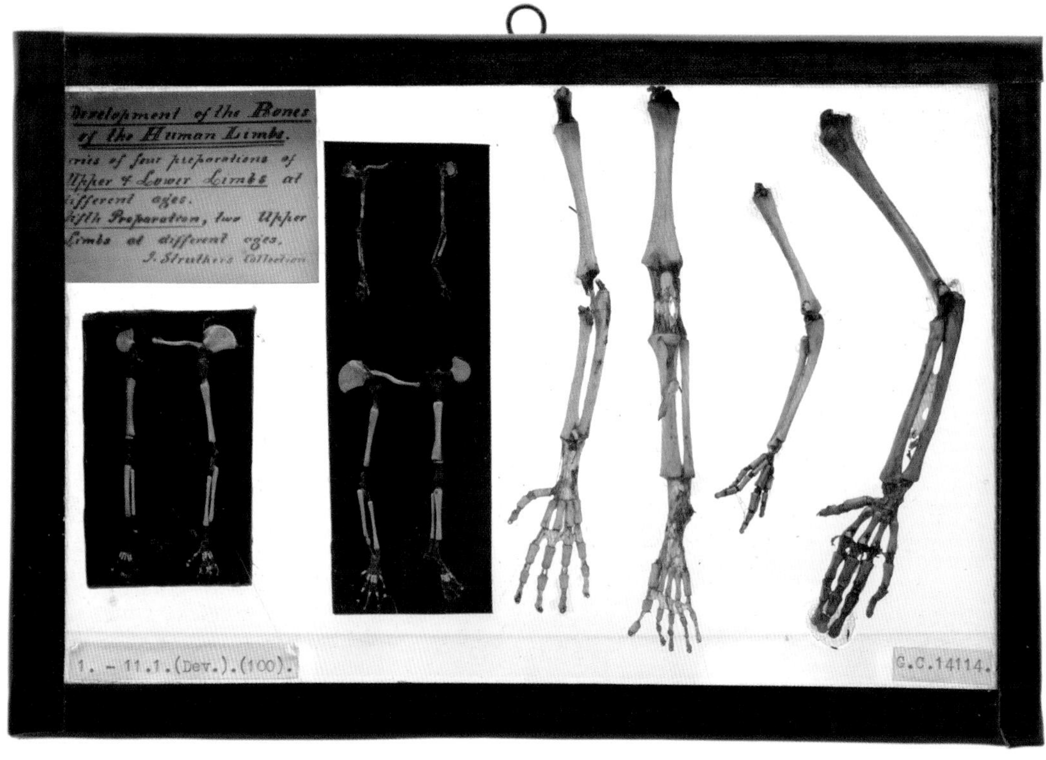

PUBLISHED BY
The Royal College of Surgeons of Edinburgh, 2009

ISBN 0954621360

FUNDED BY
The Recognition Scheme, a Scottish Government initiative managed by Museums Galleries Scotland

DESIGNED BY
contagious

PRINTED BY
Allander
PRINT UNLIMITED

PHOTOGRAPHY
MARC MARNIE
except where noted.

Above: **Foetal limb development.** Struthers Collection. GC 14114.
Opposite: **Lymph vessels** of a portion of the jejunem injected with mercury. Bell Collection. BC.xii.5.N.4 GC 12073.

Surgeons' Hall

A MUSEUM ANTHOLOGY

Dawn Kemp *with* Sara Barnes

President's Foreword

It is always a fascinating experience to walk through Surgeons' Hall, to follow, literally, in the footsteps of such great pioneers of surgery as Joseph Lister, at one time a curator of the Museum. It is an inspiration for aspiring surgeons, and a reminder of Sir Isaac Newton's observation that, 'If I have seen further than others, it is by standing upon the shoulders of giants.'

For many surgeons the Pathology Museum is where we sat our Fellowship examinations, being grilled by examiners who asked us, as Conan Doyle mischievously surmised, 'the Devil Knows What.'

If I were to select my favourite historical characters from the Museum's history it would be Arthur Conan Doyle and his teacher, Joseph Bell, Doyle's inspiration for his great fictional character Sherlock Holmes. Joseph Bell was President of this College and the first surgeon to the Royal Hospital for Sick Children in Edinburgh, at its current site in Sciennes Road, my surgical home for many years. We are connected through a continuum of surgeons at 'Sick Kids' who went on to serve this College – Harold Stiles, John Fraser, James Mason Brown and Andrew Wilkinson, to name but a few.

The Museum's collections have been at the heart of learning in this College for over two hundred years. Changes in surgical training and assessment have led the College and the Conservators of the Museum to seek new ways of making the collections most relevant to contemporary surgical teaching. Towards the end of the 20th century, the Museum's importance appeared to be mostly historical, but with the development of new techniques in tissue analysis and body imaging the pathological specimens have gained a new relevance in modern clinical research.

The increasing interest of the public in surgery has encouraged a growing number of visits; thus Surgeons' Hall Museum has a bright future as a unique learning resource for medical and lay audiences alike.

John D Orr President RCSEd

◀ **Mr John Orr,** President of the Royal College of Surgeons of Edinburgh alongside a portrait of Joseph Bell.

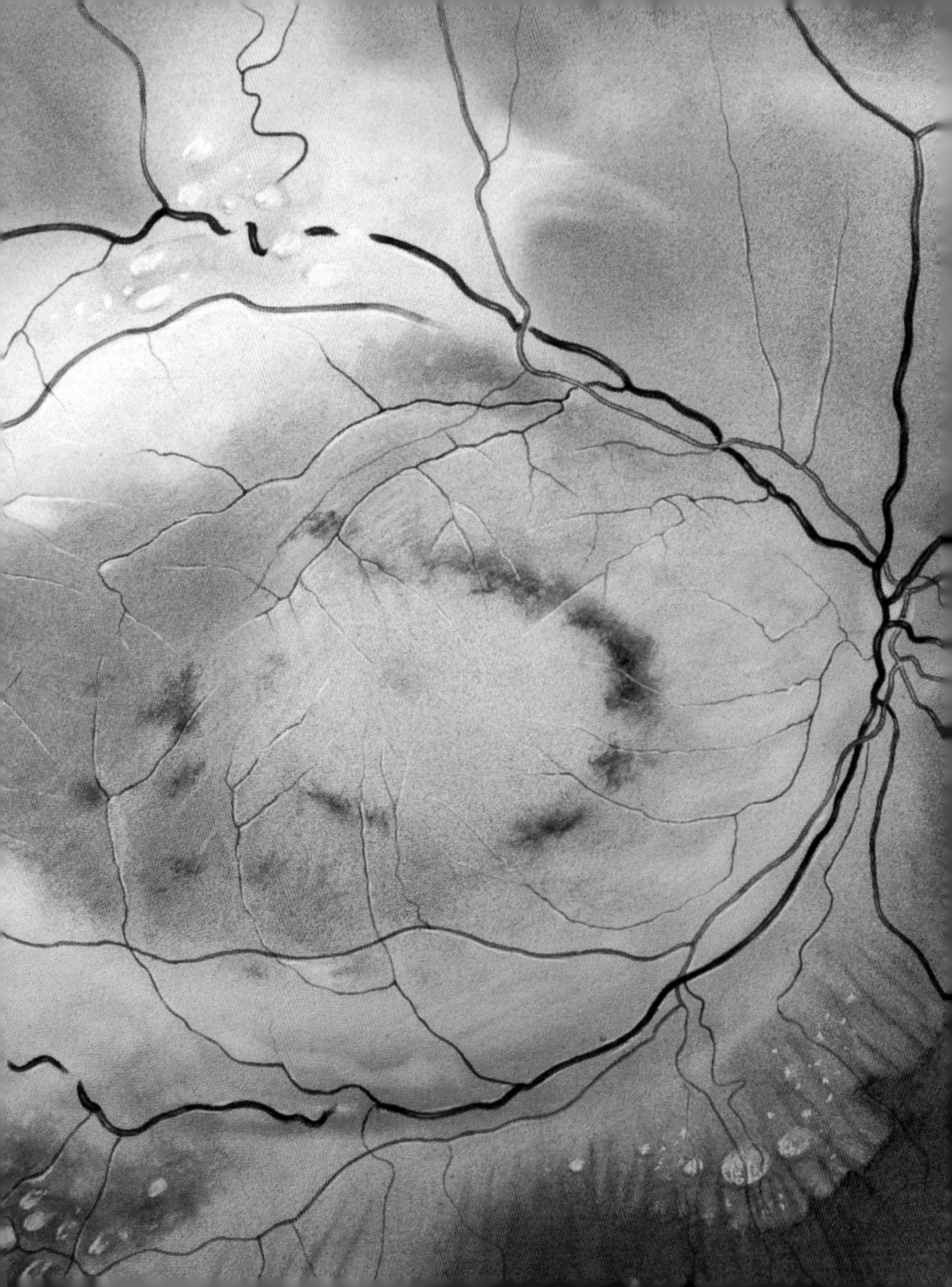

Preface

KATHLEEN JAMIE

Detail of blood vessels of the right eye by Gabriel Donald (1914-1997), c. mid 20th century. RCSEd Collections.

In the pale, airy spaces of the Surgeons' Hall Museum one encounters the dead. They are represented by their portraits, by their craft and especially, by their bodily remains. A visitor might feel wary at first, scared of the gruesome, intimidated by 'bigwigs,' but fear soon passes and one comes to realise that this Museum is not gruesome at all, it's a place of wonders and of gifts.

Every single person, adult or infant, man or woman, represented in the Museum or in this book, made us a gift, whether knowingly or not. They came from all social classes, from all over the world and from different eras. There are birds and animals too.

The portraits show anatomists and surgeons of the past, who taught or studied here. Some became famous, some were flamboyant, some were modest, some made brilliant discoveries, one or two were morally dubious, most were dedicated and driven to help their fellow people.

As well as those, there were highly skilled conservators and artists and instrument-makers, whose careful craftwork often goes unnoted. Were it not for them, there would be no Museum, we would not have any specimens or artworks or implements, some of which are hundreds of years old. There were curators and librarians, scribes and clerks too. Because of the gifts of all these people, many diseases and deformities have themselves become museum pieces. We are free of them, and the pain and shame they cause, at least in the Western world.

But at the heart of this Museum, and this book, there is another gift. I mean that given by the multitude who are anonymous: the dead who were dissected, or whose skin, or bones, or tissue were preserved as teaching aids. We learned from them, and still learn: their tender remains fascinate and move us. They teach us compassion and gratitude, and help us know what it is to be human, and to be alive.

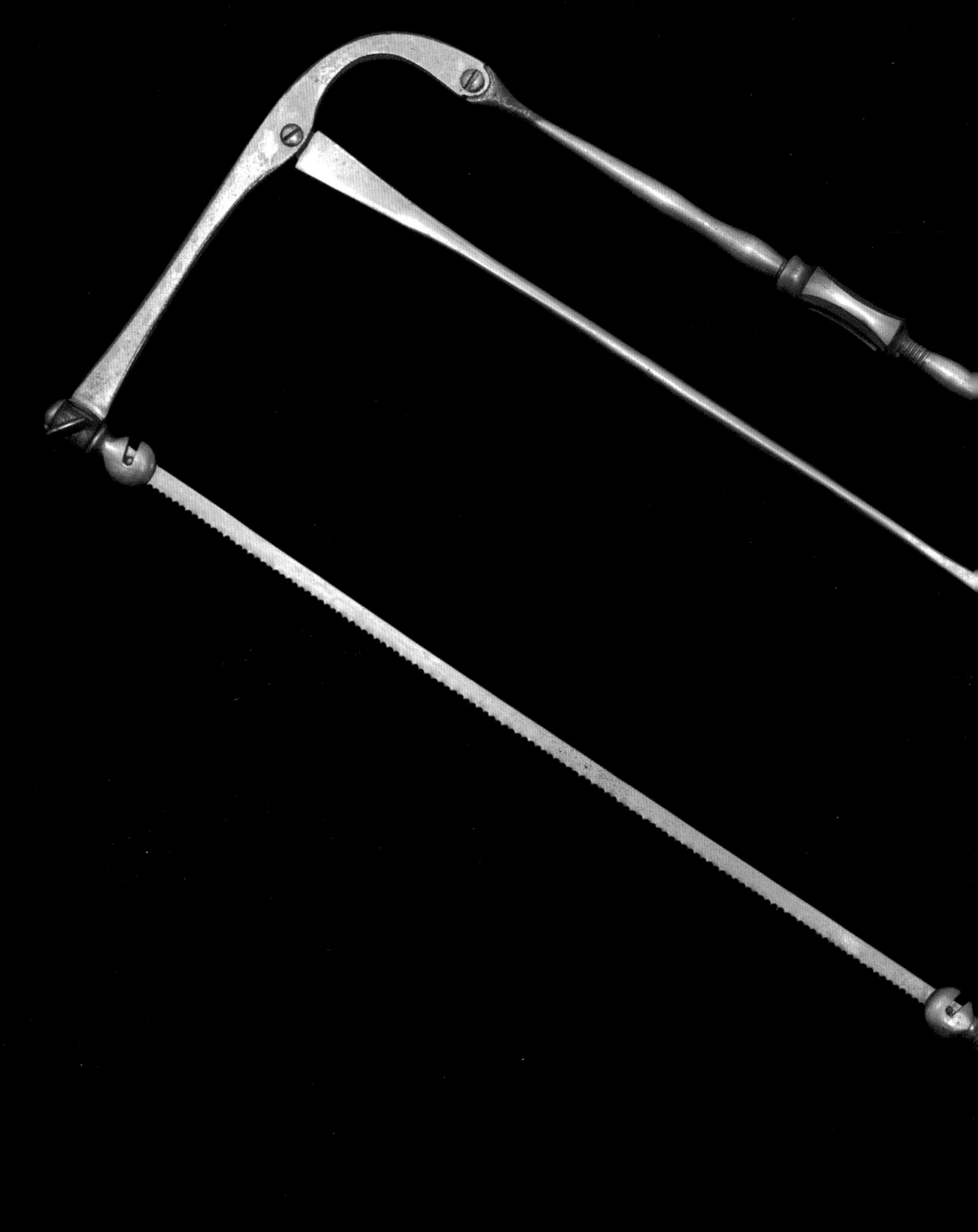

Contents

◀ Surgical orthopaedic saw. J Gardner and Son, Edinburgh, 19th century. SB 24-210.

G.C.1214.

Introduction

DAWN KEMP
DIRECTOR OF HERITAGE

All museums are made up of material fragments of history, gathered at different times by many different hands. They are a physical representation of the development of ideas, a window to imagining the past and how people who have gone before have shaped our lives today. In addition, anatomy and pathology museums, through the display of human remains can help us understand our own bodies, our own selves, in a very direct way. Even in today's world of high technology, museums of anatomy and pathology are the closest we will get to truly seeing inside ourselves; in a world saturated with virtual images of death and disease they offer a place to reflect on and regard the reality of the pain and suffering of others.

The story of Surgeons' Hall Museum is interwoven into the history of the Royal College of Surgeons of Edinburgh, the oldest medical organisation of its kind. It has played a major role in establishing Scotland as one of the world's leading centres of medicine.

Medicine, dealing as it does with matters of life and death, is a dramatic saga of human history. It is little wonder its study has influenced and inspired many writers and artists, whose work, like that of the surgeon, the physician and the anatomist rests on keen observation. They all help us look a little more closely.

This anthology is a signpost to the significant collections within Surgeons' Hall Museum and some of the people who influenced its development. It is also a collection in itself: of extracts from charters and catalogues; letters and reports; novels, plays and poems – all connected in some way to Surgeons' Hall.

There are further routes to take in finding out about the history of the Royal College of Surgeons of Edinburgh and Surgeons' Hall Museum; you may want to start by visiting the Museum website and the online collections database at: www.museum.rcsed.ac.uk

Finally, this book has been very much a collective effort. My special thanks go to Sara Barnes, Andrew Connell, marc marnie, Kathleen Jamie, Allan Carswell, Marianne Smith, Andrew Morgan, Steven Kerr, Emma Black, Ewen Griffiths and LG.

Specimens prepared by Dr Robert Knox, 1820s.
RCSEd Collections.

...of all natural and artificial curiosities

1505-1803

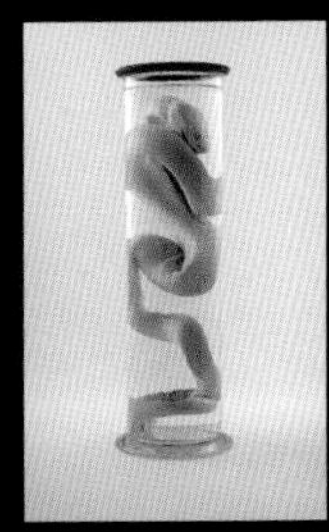

SPECIMEN OF A SNAKE.
RCSED COLLECTIONS.

39 Thay dar nocht nor will nocht brek nor dissobey in na poynt agane the samyn nor yit mak alteratioun nor innovatioun thairupon but avyse of the kingis hienes and his parliament And as for the saidis craftismen It is consentit that thay have respect to thaime all previlegeis in tyme to cum siclik as thay and thair predecessouris was had in wont and use in tymes bygane in als far as thay concerne the commoun wele and effect And at the nixt parliament thay sall avyse with the kingis grace and his lordis thairof tuiching the said mater

The coppie of the Barbouris sele of cause as followis

To all and sindrie to quhais knawlege thir present lettres sall cum The provost baillies and counsale of the burgh of Edinburgh greting in God everlesting Witt your universiteis that the day of the dait of thir presentis Compeirit befoir us sittand in Jugement in the tolbuith of the said burgh the kirkmaisteris and brether of the Surregianis and barbouris within the samin And presentit till us thair bill and supplicatioun Desyring us for the lovyng of God honour of oure Soverane Lord and all his lieges And for worschip and policy of this burgh and for the gude reule and ordour tobe had and maid amangis the saidis craftis in tymes to cum That we wald grant and consent to thame thir previlegeis reulis and statutis contenit in thair said bill and supplicatioun quhilk eftir followis To your my lordis Provost baillies and worthy Counsale of this gude toun richt humblie menis and schawis your daylie servitouris The kirkmaisteris and brether of Surregianis and barbouris within this burgh That quhair we wald it war wele knawin till all your wisdomes quhou that we uphald ane altar situat within your college kirk of Sanct Geill in the honour of God and Sanct Mungow our patroun and hes na importance to uphald the samin bot oure sober oulklie penny and upsettis quhilk ar small in effect till sustene and uphald oure said altar in all necessar thingis convenient thairto And becaus we ar and evir was of gude mynde till do this gude toun all the steid plesour and service that we can or may baith in walking and warding stenting and bering of all oure portabill chargeis within this burgh at all tymes as oure nichtbouris and craftis dois within the samin We desyre at your lordschippis and wisdomes till gif and grant to us and oure successouris thir reulis statutis and previlegeis underwrittin quhilkis ar consonant to resoun honour till oure soverane lord and all his lieges proffitabill and agreabill to this gude toune In the first that we micht have yeirlie chosin amangis us ane kirkmaister and oursman To quhome the haill brether of the craftis forsaid sall obey for that yeir. Item that na maner of persoun occupie nor use ony poyntis of oure saidis craftis of Surregerie or barbour craft within this burgh bot gif he be first frieman and burges of the samin and that he be worthy and expert in all the poyntis belangand the saidis craftis diligentlie and avysitlie examinit and admittit be the maisteris of the said craft for the honorabill serving of oure Soverane lord his lieges and nychtbouris of this burgh And als that everie man that is tobe maid frieman and maister amangis us be examinit and previt in thir poyntis following that is to say that he knaw anatomea nature and complexioun of every member

From Here Health 1505-1696

The Royal College of Surgeons of Edinburgh was founded in 1505 as the Incorporation of Surgeon Barbers of Edinburgh, making it the oldest medical fellowship of its kind in the world.

Its Seal of Cause (charter) from the Town of Edinburgh set out what the freemen must do and know to be good at their work. In support of this, the town was to give the incorporation one dead body a year for anatomical dissection, an essential element of study for both apprentice and practicing surgeons. The Seal of Cause stated:

'that no manner of person employ nor use any points of our said crafts of surgery or barber craft within this burgh unless he is first a freeman and burgess of the same; and that he be worthy and expert in all the subjects belonging to the said crafts, diligently and knowledgeably examined and admitted by the masters of the said craft for the honourable serving of our Sovereign Lord, his lieges and inhabitants of this burgh; and also that every man that is to be made freeman and master amongst us be examined and approved in these following points, that is to say, that he know anatomy, the nature and complexion of every member of the human body, and likewise that he know all the veins of the same, that he may perform phlebotomy in due time; and also that he know in which member the sign has domination for the time, for every man ought to know the nature and substance of every thing with which he deals, or else he is negligent; and that we may have once a year a condemned man after death to perform anatomy on, whereby we may have experience, each one to instruct others, and we shall do suffrage for the soul; and that no barber, master nor servant, within this burgh practice, use nor exercise the craft of Surgery without he be expert and know perfectly the things described above;'

King James IV of Scotland confirmed the Town of Edinburgh's charter to the Incorporation of Surgeon Barbers in 1506, giving it royal approval.

Extract from the 1505 'Seal of Cause' (charter) from the Town of Edinburgh to the Surgeon Barbers, written in old Scots. Courtesy Edinburgh City Archives.

In my defens

James IV to his Treasurer

EDWIN MORGAN

Portrait of James IV (1473-1513), after copy by Daniel Mytens (c. 1590-1647), Henry Woolford, 1955. RCSEd Collections. Photo Max McKenzie.

Oh for Christ's sake gie the signor his siller.
Alchemist my erse, but he's hermless, is he no?
He'll never blaw us up in oor beds, I tak it.
If makkin wings is his new-fanglt ploy
It'll no cost the earth – a wheen o skins,
Or silk if he can get it, wid for the struts,
Fedders, is he intae fedders?, gum, oh aye,
Ane prentice or twa, keep their mooths shut,
It micht be kinrik secret stuff, ye ken,
Fleg the enemy, sky black wi baukie-birds,
My Gode, whit could ye no drap on thaim –
This signor, whit's he cried, Damiano,
Tell him he'll get his purse, but tell him:
Nae mair elixirs, quintessences, *faux* gowd!

Ye say he wants tae loup frae the castle-waws
At Stirling. Weel weel, that's a dandy step,
And lat the warld tak tent o sic a ferlie.
But jist suppose there's a doonbeat scenario
For Signor Damiario: ane wing snapt aff,
He faws, he breks a leg, it's a richt scunner.
Signor, help is at haun! Ane speedy litter
Wheechs him tae Edinburgh, whaur the new College
O Surgeons walcomes him with aipen erms.
I'll be there, signor, a king can set a leg.
I need mair practice, but I can dae it, oh yes.
And noo for the warst-case scenario:
The bird-man whuds doon splat, doon tae his daith.
Oh what a bonus: we'll hae ane public dissection.
My charter will hae wings, it'll tak aff,
Whit can we no dae gif we set oor minds tae it?
Tell Signor Damiano, be he limpin or be he a corp,
The College o Surgeons stauns honed and skeely and eident.

Edwin Morgan's poem, in Scots, refers to the Italian John Damian, alchemist to James IV who famously tried to fly by attaching chicken feathers to his arms and jumping from the battlements of Stirling Castle.

HINC SANITAS
COLLEGIUM
REGIUM CHIRURGORUM
EDINENSE
DIPLOMATE REGIO CONSTITUTUM
A·D · MDV·

Armorial Bearings

In 1672 the Incorporation of surgeon barbers was granted its own armorial bearings (coat of arms). It is a wonderfully rich and dramatic badge and tells a pictorial story of the founding and principles of the surgeons' incorporation.

The Honourable Colledge of Chirurgeons of Edinburgh

Gives for Ensignes Armoriall:
'Azur a humaine Body fess wayes Betwixt a dexter hand having ane eye on the Palme issuing out of ane cloud downward and a Castle Situate on a rock all proper within a bordur Or Charged with severall Instruments peculiar to the Art On a Canton as the first A St Andrews cross argent surmounted of a thistle vert Crowned as the third: Above the shield ane helmet befitting their degree mantled azure doubled Or And for their crest on a wreath Or and Azur The sun dissipating a cloud proper Supported be Aesculapius vested argent mantled azur crowned with a Laurell Holding in his hand a baston nue reaching down to his foot wreathed about a Serpent proper armed gules and Hypocrates vested as the other with a mantle gules And on his head a Bonnet sable holding in his left hand a book expanded both standing on a Compartment And for their motto in ane escroll above all Hinc sanitas.'

Register of Arms Vol 1. Pt 3. c 1672.
Kept in the Lord Lyon's Office, Edinburgh.

RCSEd Armorial Bearings, Stained Glass, Surgeons' Hall, 1897. The Latin motto *Hinc Sanitas* shown above the coat of arms means in English: From here, health. Photo Max McKenzie.

1
4
2
3
6
2
7
2
5
2

1. the sun dissipating a cloud

The Sun, in ancient legends, is the restorer of life. It brings light and removes the darkness cast by the cloud. The sun wages continual battle against the demons of drought, darkness and illness. It represents enlightenment and learning.

2. severall Instruments peculiar to the Art

The instruments represent the tools of the surgeon barbers' craft.

The armorial bearings on the College Officer's silver badge, dating from 1698 show: saws and knives; trepanning drills; fleams and lancets; razors; a cup – perhaps used for bleeding; hooks; needles; a strop for sharpening blades and retractors.

3. a St Andrews cross…surmounted of a thistle…Crowned

The cross of St Andrew, Scotland's patron saint and a thistle are emblems of Scotland. The Crown indicates King James IV's ratification, in 1506, of the charter granted to the Incorporation of Surgeon Barbers by the town of Edinburgh.

4. ane helmet befitting their degree

The helmet or helm is a symbol used in heraldry to indicate a knight. The cloth around represents the cloak or coat knights wore to protect their armour from the sun. Armorial bearings were used like badges to identify knights and were later sewn on to their cloaks – hence. 'Coat of Arms.'

5. a Castle Situate on a rock

The Castle represents Edinburgh and recognises the 'Seal of Cause' (charter) presented to the surgeon barbers by the Town in 1505, incorporating them as an official craft guild.

6. a dexter hand having ane eye on the Palme

A right hand with an eye on the palm is a symbol of the 'healing hand' associated with medicine. The word surgery comes from the Greek for hand (cheir) and work (ergon). 'The Hand That Sees' might be a further reference to the surgeon's hand working, as if it had sight, inside the human body.

7. a humaine Body fess wayes

The human body, lying horizontally, likely represents anatomical dissection and the need for surgeons to know the anatomy of the human body, a condition of the Surgeon Barbers' seal of cause that 'every man that is to be made freeman and master amongst us be examined and…that he know anatomy, the nature and complexion of every member of the human body…'

◀ **Armorial Bearings of the Royal College of Surgeons of Edinburgh.** Carved and painted wood thought to have been made for St Giles High Kirk. RCSEd Collections.

Anatomy Class

SUHAYL SAADI

'We had a whole human body to dissect over a period of eighteen months. As the corpus of our knowledge slowly grew, the corpse before us steadily shrank.

In those days (the early 1980s) we were encouraged not to wear gloves. As a teenage medical student, cutting up, pulling apart and examining every last millimetre of this body, spending more time in intimate contact with it than I had spent with any other being, it began to dawn on me that the flesh beneath my fingers, the brain half-floating in the glass jar, was actually a person who had given permission for me to dissect her in this manner and that for me this was an unimaginable privilege. In spite of the thousands of living bodies that I have examined and treated over the years since, this one corpse – her smell, her texture, the sounds and shadows of her slow dismemberment – lingers most powerfully in my memory, in the prints of my fingers. I never knew her name, nor the slightest detail concerning her life, yet after meeting her, I was never able to view the human body, or life, in the same way again. In a sense, her humanity had been stolen. But she took my innocence.'

Specimen of human brain.
RCSEd Collections. GC 4963.

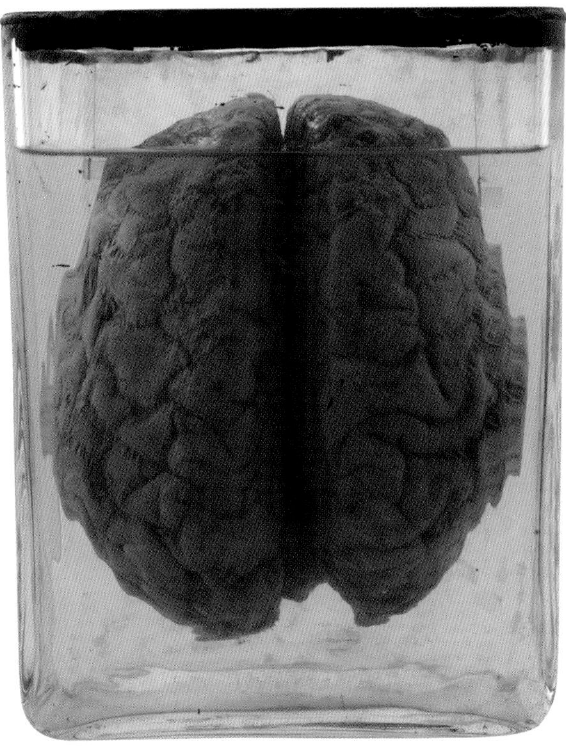

Anatomical Demonstration, Rotterdam by the Dutch artist A. Van der Groes, 1702.
RCSEd Collections.

Bodies for Anatomy

By the mid 17th century one body a year was no longer enough to meet the surgeons' teaching needs. In 1678 a body taken from a grave in Edinburgh's Greyfriars Church was reported likely to have been:

'*...stolen away by some chirurgeon* [surgeon], *or his servant, to make ane anatomicale dissection on.*'
Lord Fountainhall ms: 1678.

And in 1694 The Incorporation of Surgeons asked the Town Council for:

'*the dead bodies of foundlings who die betwixt the time they are weaned and their being put to schools or trades...also ...the dead bodies of such as are felo de se, when it is found unquestionable self-murder and have none to own them...*'
Burgh Records of Edinburgh, November 1694.

The Town offered the 'gift' of such bodies on condition that the surgeons build before Michaelmass (September 29) 1697 '*ane anatomicall Theatre where they shall have once a year...ane publick anatomicall dissection...and if they failzie thir presents to be voyd and null.*'

▲ Gravestone, Greyfriars Kirkyard, 1679.
Photo Max McKenzie.

The first collections 1697-1804

The Surgeon Barbers met the conditions of the Town Council of Edinburgh and by the end of 1697 had built a dedicated Hall, where public anatomical dissections could take place. The Incorporation, now with a fine new building by the celebrated architect James Smith, was firmly established as one of the country's leading medical organisations. Portraits of members of the Incorporation were commissioned to decorate the new Surgeons' Hall and it was decided that the College Officer, a post dating back to 1505, should wear a livery coat and a silver badge. The badge made in 1698 is the oldest representation of the Incorporation's armorial bearings.

▲ **Surgeons' Hall** designed by James Smith and opened in 1697. The Hall was built to accommodate an anatomical theatre where public dissections could be held once a year. Engraving by P. Fourdrinier from a drawing by Paul Sandby. RCSEd Collections.

▶ **College Officer's Silver Badge** showing the Incorporation's armorial bearings, 1698. RCSEd Collections. Photo Max McKenzie.

Mr James Kirkwood — Given by Mr James Kirkwood Kirkwood's Grammatica nova Epistolarum & Gloria [illegible]

Wm Ross — Given by Wm Ross Vintner A booke for Bathing

Mr Herbert Kennedy professor of philosophie — Given by Mr Herbert Kennedy the books following viz
Keckermanni Systema philosophicum 2 vol.
Bellarmini Controversiae Religionis
Sir Walter Davenants Works
Balzac anent Adoration
Grammaire de M. Sudin
Johnstons animadv. on the physicall treatises
Arnolds manuall of [illegible] admirabilium
Dr [illegible] anent Religion

William Bishop — Given by William Bishop the books following viz
A fine English Bible 8vo
A[nother] bible with the psalmes
Riverius the whole practice of physick with observations
Anatomie de M. [illegible]
Celsi tractatus medicina
Cornelius Agrippa of the vanity of all sciences
Barroughs method of physick
The physicians practice
[illegible] de l'amendement de vie

James Allan — Given by James Allan Vintner The Acts of Parliament from K. Ja: 1. to 2 parl. Charl. 2.

Mr Pat Mowbray — Given by Mr Patrick Mowbray Clerk to the incorporation of the Chirurgion Apothecaries a pair of a [illegible] [illegible] in [illegible] [illegible] long

Mr Ja. Sutherland — Given by Mr James Sutherland professor of Botany Parkinsons Theatrum Botanicum

Dr John Ramsay — Given by Dr John Ramsay Doctor of Medicine the books following viz
Ki. Hobokeni Anatom. Secundin. Humanae
Severini Pinaei de not. Virginitatis una cum Tractat. Lud.
Bonaccioli de foetus formatione
Jo. Pecqueti Experim. Anatomica
Joseph. Quercetani Opera Medica

Thomas Veitch — Given by Thomas Veitch Chirurgeon Apothecary The Rivalls by Geo: D. of Albemarle
Confessio fidei

Act appointing commissioners with the said Chirurgions of [illegible] at Coupar upon the [illegible] of Apryle next. Commissioners to meet with the said Chirurgions of [illegible] at Coupar 12 Aprile next

Eodem die The Deacon represented to the Calling that the occasion of the meeting was that they might appoint some Commissioners to goe and [illegible] conform to agreement betwixt the Calling & the Chirurgions of Fyfe dated the [illegible] day of July 1693 to meet with the said Chirurgions of Fyfe at Coupar upon the [illegible] day of Aprile next being the 12th day of the said month and for that effect caused read the Acts & [illegible] containing the articles of the said agreement Conform whereunto the Calling nominated & appointed Alexander Monteith and Walter Porterfield to be Commissioners for that effect and appoints Alexander Wilson [illegible] of Thomas Dunlop & [illegible] [illegible] Doctor James [illegible] [illegible] [illegible] Gideon Eliot [illegible] [illegible] James Hamilton George Kirkton to [illegible] [illegible] [illegible] [illegible] or any other the Deacon shall think fitt to call [illegible] three with the Deacon to be a quorum to [illegible] of the Commission & instructions and ordains the said Committee to bring in an draught of the [illegible] & constitutions for the [illegible] [illegible] against the next meeting of the Calling to be considered by the said Calling whereupon this Act is made &c

Act for bringing in draught of the [illegible] for the [illegible]

Eodem die The Calling ordains the Clerk to [illegible] [illegible] of the diplomata and to send them [illegible] with the Commissioners to be given to [illegible] of the Chirurgions of Fyfe as are already [illegible] up and [illegible] not gotten them as yet the said Chirurgions of Fyfe paying the Clerks & Officers [illegible] the fees [illegible] [illegible] [illegible] to the Clerk [illegible] and [illegible] this Act is made.

Act for [illegible] the diplomata to [illegible] of the Chirurgions of Fyfe as are already [illegible] up and [illegible] not [illegible] given them

Followes the [illegible] of the diploma

At Edr the 23 day of March 1699 years The [illegible] day The Deacon being conveened & taking to [illegible] the [illegible] qualifications & good [illegible] of John Arnot Chirurgion Apothecarie in Coupar with the [illegible] of Fyfe and being certainly informed that he [illegible] past [illegible] he has exercised the art of Chirurgery & Pharmacie in that place (with the blessing of God upon his endeavours) with very good success to the great satisfaction & approbation of the [illegible] [illegible] [illegible] [illegible] wee doe therefore authorize & [illegible] the said John

The development of library and museum collections for the new Hall was begun in earnest in 1699 when an advert was placed in the Edinburgh Gazette giving notice that:

'*...the Chirurgeon Apothecaries of Edinburgh are erecting a Library of Physicall, Anatomicall, Chirurgicall, Botanicall, Pharmaceuticall and other curious books. Also they are making a Collection of all natural and artificiall curiosities. If any person have such to bestow let them give notice to Walter Porterfield present Treasurer to the Society...who will cause their names to be honourably recorded and if they think not fit to bestow them gratis they shall have reasonable prices for them.*'

A committee was appointed to draw up rules about how the new collections were to be recorded and used. The first rules in October 1699 included the stipulations that donors would be given due recognition; the library should be open two hours per day and 'No person shall be allowed to drink or smoke tobacco in the library.' Additional Laws added in May 1709 ordered:

'*...That two Catalogues of the Curiosities and Chirurgicall instruments be made up by the above Commitee qch are to be keeped subscrived and annually revised as the books of the Library. And no curiosity to be trusted out off the Library keepers sight*

...That any of the Chirurgicall instruments may be lent to a master he giveing his obligation to return the same within eight days with a penalty above the value of the Chirurgicall instrument lent to be booked in the same manner as these given for the books.'

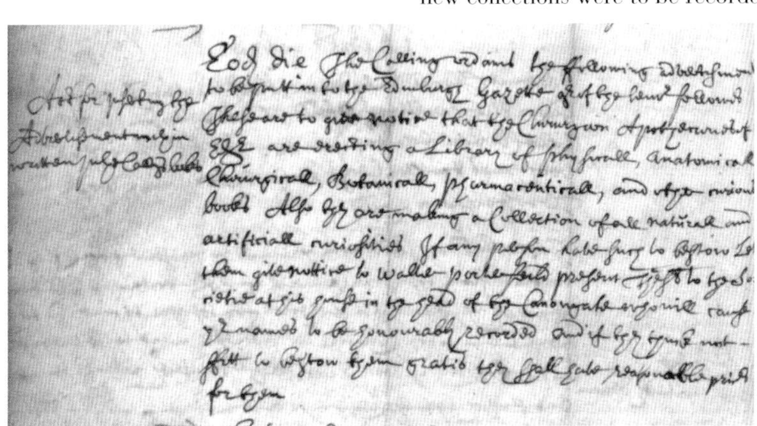

▲ **Extract from the College Minutes 1699,** recording the placing of an advert in the Edinburgh Gazette requesting donations or purchases of books and curiosities for the Incorporation.

◀ **Extract from the College Minutes, 23 March 1699.**
Index list of 'Gifts to the Calling.'
RCSEd Collections.

Gifts listed include:
A case containing ten old German lancets,
A large eel skin stuft and taken from Cramond Water, A pair of tenailes incisive and a pair of tenailes for drawing of teeth,
A pair of Scots cock spurs, clecked in Fife, prodigiously long,
An American birds beak (very curious),
An Allegatory or young crocodile.

The Medina Portraits

When the Incorporation of Surgeons relocated to their new Hall in 1697, a series of portraits of all its members was commissioned from John Baptiste de Medina (1659-1710). Medina, a painter of Flemish-Spanish origin, had previously had a studio in London and among his clients counted several members of the Scottish aristocracy.

He arrived in Edinburgh for a short trip during 1693-4 in order to paint members of their families, but he was to stay for the rest of his life.

Medina (later to become Sir John – he was the last man to be knighted in Scotland before the Act of Union in 1707) produced over 30 oval shaped potraits of the surgeons between 1697 and c.1708. As a group they create a unique historical record of a medical community of the period. In 1708 at the invitation of the Incorporation, Medina added his own self-portrait – recognition of the professional friendship between the artist and his medical subjects. He is buried in Greyfriars' Kirkyard in Edinburgh.

Self Portrait by Sir John Baptiste de Medina, 1708.
RCSEd Collections.

Anatomical Dissection

The first recorded anatomical dissection to take place in Surgeons' Hall was in November 1702. The body dissected was that of David Myles, who was sentenced to death after being convicted of incest with his sister. The dissection, presided over by Archibald Pitcairne, took over a week.

Day 1: Anatomy in general, dissection and demonstration of the common teguments and muscles of the abdomen (James Hamilton – current deacon)

Day 2: The peritoneum, omentum, stomach, intestines, mesentry and pancreas (John Baillie)

Day 3: Liver, spleen, kidneys, ureters, bladder and parts of generation (Alexander Monteith)

Day 4: Brain and its membranes with discourse of the animal spirits (David Fyfe)

Day 5: Muscles of the extremeties (Hugh Paterson)

Day 6: Skeleton in general, with the head (Robert Clerk)

Day 7: The articulation of the rest of the skeleton (James Auchinleck)

Day 8: Epilogue (Archibald Pitcairne)

College Minutes, 1702.

James Hamilton

John Baillie

David Fyfe

Hugh Paterson

Robert Clerk

James Auchinleck

Archibald Pitcairne

The portraits shown were all painted by Sir John de Medina between 1697 and 1707, except that of Robert Clerk which is attributed to Medina's apprentice, William Aikman. RCSEd Collections. Photos Max McKenzie.

The Remains

DILYS ROSE

A shilpit bodie noo, a skinbane mannie,
decrepit relic fi some Hoose o Horrors,
hingin in a box ower graun ti be yir deid-kist.
A draught bestirs yir shanks: yie gie a weary jig.
Yi're missin a fit, an airm, an aw yon flesh
yi sinned agin yir ain wi. If yi did. An if
yi didny, an if, kis yi hidny ony space
fur the bairns tae courie doon thirsels,
they lay atween thir mither an thir faither,
an if the warm braith o yir eldest dochter
on yir neck, made yi tak her fur yir bidie-in,
yi war aye ower beat by then fur mair'n a cuddle,
an if, forby, the kirk jist hud a muckle drouth for sin –
onieweys, yi swung for it. Yi're swingin still.
Yir sins o turpitude or poverty, an whit
they brocht – the raip, the spade, the saw –
hae made yi gey weel-kent amang chirugeons.
They've split yi intae aa yir pairts then pit yi
(maistly) back thegither. They've kent yir liver
inside oot, yir hert, yir spleen, yir cerebellum,
but nane o aa they learned bodies hud onie inklin
o whit made yi dae the things yi did. Or didny.

The remains of David Myles whose body was used for the first recorded anatomical dissection conducted at Surgeons' Hall.

These
Anatomical Pre=
=parations, were gift=
=ed, to the Incorporation of
Chyrurgion Apothecaries
of Edr, by Alexr Monro, 1718.

The Monros

Critics – appalled, I venture on the name,
Those cut-throat bandits in the paths of fame:
Bloody dissectors, worse than ten Monroes;
He hacks to teach, they mangle to expose.

ROBERT BURNS, *'To Robert Graham of Fintry, Esq,'* 1791.

John Monro (1670-1740) by William Aikman, 1715. RCSEd Collections.

The oldest skeleton in Surgeons' Hall collections was prepared by Alexander Monro *primus* (1697-1767) and presented in 1719. Alexander was the son of John Monro (1670-1740), Deacon (President) of the College of Surgeons from 1712 to 1714, and considered to be the founder of the Medical School at Edinburgh University.

John did much to advance his son's medical career in Edinburgh and promoted the anatomical work he had undertaken in London in 1717:

'A great number of Preparations of the different Organs, the Fruits of these Dissections, were sent home by A.M to his Father ... The Father vain of his Son's Performances showed them to many curious People who asked to see them and at the solicitation of the College of Physicians and the Board of Surgeons made a Present of many of them to these Societies to be put in their Repositories.'

Life of Dr Ar. Monro Sr in his own handwriting. Manuscript held in the University of Otago, New Zealand.

Alexander Monro *primus* (1697-1767) attributed to Allan Ramsay. Private Collection.

Dissected skeleton given by Alexander Monro *primus* to the College of Surgeons in 1718. RCSEd Collections.

In 1721 Alexander became the Professor of Anatomy at Edinburgh University, followed by his son, Alexander Monro *secundus*(1733-1817) and grandson, Alexander Monro *tertius* (1773-1859). The Monros were to monopolise the teaching of anatomy at the University until 1846.

'the Picture(s) in the Surgeons' Hall there of the present Professors... excellently Done ... tis the best Collection of heads done by him.'

GEORGE VERTUE, the English antiquary, referring to Medina's paintings of the surgeons, 1721.

James Douglas, 4th Duke of Hamilton by John de Medina, 1703. RCSEd Collections.

Surgeons' Hall and its collections became something of an attraction for visitors to the city as well as local people.

In the early 1720s Daniel Defoe visited Surgeons' Hall and later wrote:

'...I must not omit the seminaries of learning... the first of them is the surgeons hall, or surgeon-apothecaries, for here they make but one profession. They have set up a large building all at their own charge, in which is their great hall, hung round with the pictures of all the surgeons of the city, that are, or have been since the building was erected as also the pictures of Duke Hamilton and the late Lord Chancellor. They have also a Chamber of Rarities, a theatre for dissections, and the finest bagnio in Britain; 'tis perfectly well contrived, and exactly well finished, no expence [sic] being spared to make it both convenient and effectually useful.

In their Chamber of Rarities they have several skeletons of strange creatures, a mummy, and other curious things, too many to be particular in them here.'

DANIEL DEFOE, *A tour thro' the whole island of Great Britain*, 1726.

James Ogilvie, Viscount Seafield (1664-1730) by Sir Godfrey Kneller, c. 1700. Ogilvie was Lord Chancellor of Scotland from 1702 to 1704 and again from 1705 to 1708. RCSEd Collections.

Egyptian mummified head, date unknown. RCSEd Collections.

‘many other curiosities’

By 1763, due to financial pressures, the surgeons were forced to rent out part of their Hall. There was no longer space to accommodate the library and museum collections and they were transferred to the university with arrangements made for members of the College to be allowed access to the university library. Pitcairne and Monro’s anatomical preparations remained at Surgeons’ Hall and it is possible that other specimens were also kept.

The College, however, continued to accept donations to the collections and by the end of the century one of the earliest guide books to Edinburgh included an entry for Surgeons’ Hall:

‘In the place named the High School Yards, 300 feet east of the Infirmary, stands a neat building called the Surgeons Hall, erected at the charge of that Society in the city, in which is their great hall hung round with the pictures of all the eminent surgeons of this place who have flourished since the building formed. Here they have also a theatre for dissections, and a chamber of rarities, in which are several skeletons of uncommon creatures, a mummy, and many other curiosities.’

ALEXANDER KINCAID, *The Traveller’s Companion Through the City of Edinburgh*, 1794.

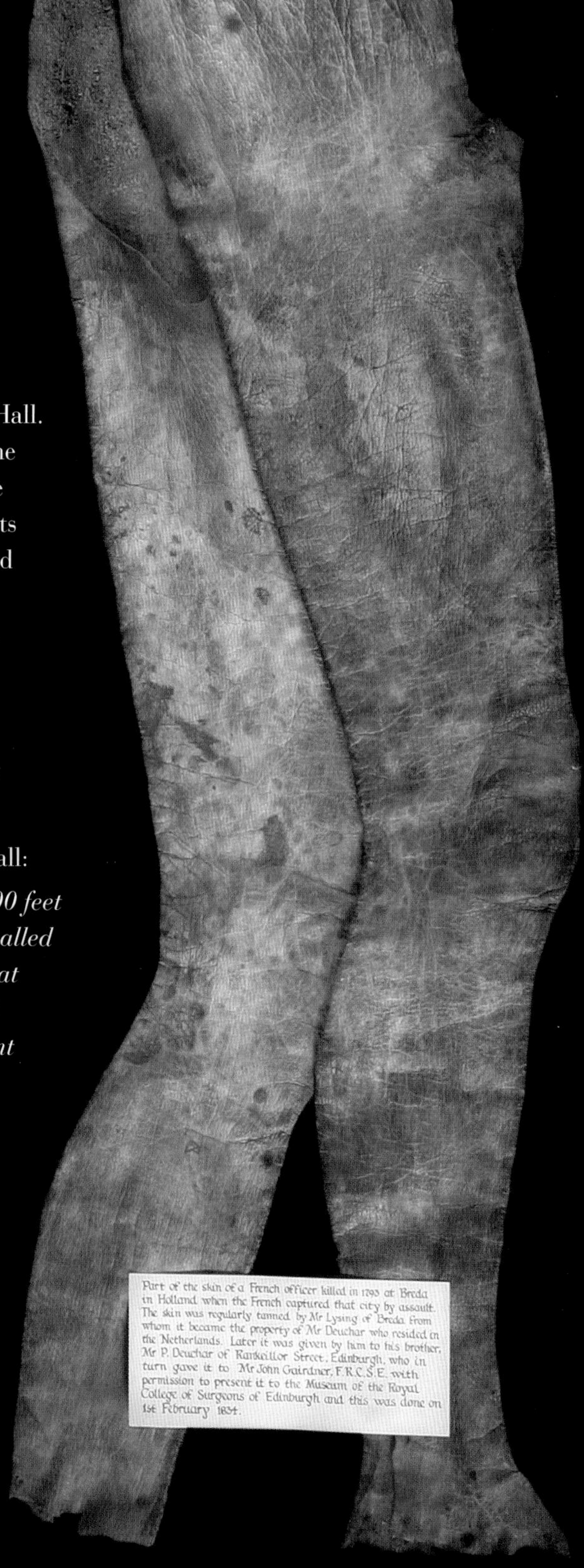

Skin of French Officer’s legs from the Battle of Breda 1793. RCSEd Collections. Photo Max McKenzie.

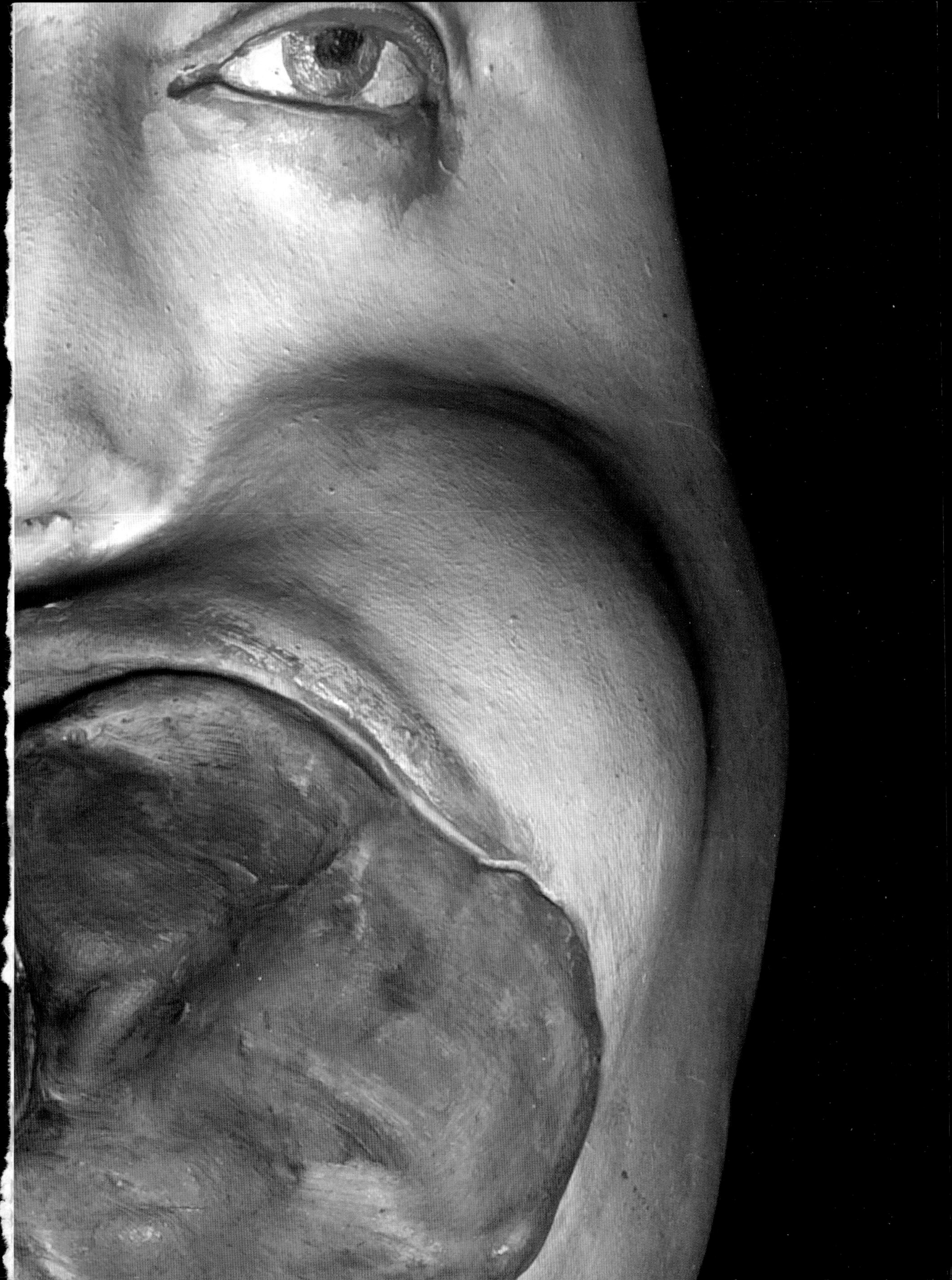

▲ Surgeons' Hall, 1697. Artist of building unknown, figures by or after John Kay, c.1796. RCSEd Collections.

Old Surgeons' Hall and John Kay

The figures in the foreground, except Dr Joseph Black (chemist) and Sir James Stirling, are all prominent Edinburgh medical men. They are:

1 Dr Joseph Black, 1728 - 1799.
2 Mr John Bennet, 1740 - 1805.
3 Dr William Cullen, 1710 - 1790.
4 Mr Alexander Wood, 1727 - 1807.
5 Mr Alexander Hamilton, 1739 - 1802.
6 Prof Alexander Monro *secundus*, 1733 - 1817.
7 Mr Benjamin Bell, 1749 - 1806.
8 Dr Thomas Hay, 1752 - 1816, (Deacon of the College of Surgeons, 1794-1796).
9 Sir James Stirling, 1740 - 1805, (Lord Provost of Edinburgh, 1792-1796).
10 Prof Francis Home, 1719 - 1813.
11 Prof Andrew Duncan Snr, 1744 - 1828.

John Kay qualified as a barber in Edinburgh in the mid 1700s. He went on to create the finest visual record of Edinburgh social life in the late eighteenth /early nineteenth century.

Most of the figures in the painting were originally produced and sold by Kay as individual portraits between 1784 and 1796. The portraits of Thomas Hay and Sir James Stirling, the Lord Provost of Edinburgh, both date from 1796. This could suggest they were specially made for inclusion in this painting, which would tie in with its having been commissioned to commemorate the centenary in 1797 of Surgeons' Hall.

...morbid preparations, casts and drawings

1804-1886

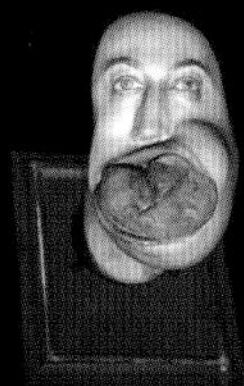

PLASTER CAST OF HEAD SHOWING TUMOUR OF LOWER JAW, 1828. RCSED COLLECTIONS.

Report continued

" be understood, that all Surgeons & Mates on the
" Staff of the Army; Surgeons in the Army and
" Surgeons Assistants and Surgeons in the Navy
" as well as Mates may attend them gratis
" on producing Certificates of their Commissions

"7 That if the Professor shall not adhere to
" these terms he shall be understood to have
" abdicated his office on proof thereof being
" given to the College, otherways it shall
" be understood that his appointment shall
" continue as long as no valid objection can be
" substantiated against him.

"8 That every vacancy of the Professorship shall
" be filled up at a meeting of the College
" expressly called for the purpose.

"9 That the Professor shall be exempted from offici-
" ating as an examinator.

"10 That it would greatly facilitate the teaching of
" Surgery and prove useful as well as creditable
" to the College to form a Museum of Morbid
" preparations, Casts, and drawings of Diseas-
" es; and that all the members of the College
" should be requested to give their assistance in
" promoting this very necessary part of the
" plan by supporting it with all such articles
" of this kind as may be in their power.

"11 That this Museum shall be the property of
" the College and be open under such Regu-
" lations as the College may adopt, to the
" inspection of all its members.

"12 That as it is the sole object of the College of
" Surgeons in establishing this Professorship,
" to promote the study and practice of Surgery
" the Professor of Clinical Surgery in the
" University, when a member of the College
" shall be allowed the use of such preparations

New Beginnings

In 1804 the Royal College of Surgeons of Edinburgh established the new post of Professor of Surgery and John Thomson was the first to be appointed. It was also proposed that a museum 'of morbid preparations, casts and drawings of diseases' should be formed to aid surgical teaching and that members should donate all they could to the collection.

The management of the museum was set out:

'That five members shall be elected annually who, along with the President and Professor of Surgery, shall form a Committee for the management of the Museum, and who shall see that everything be duly taken care of; but the trouble of preparing all morbid specimens of chirurgical diseases presented to the College and of keeping them in proper arrangement shall devolve exclusively upon the Professor.' College Minutes 5 October 1804.

The first catalogue of the collections, known as the General Catalogue (GC) was started around 1807. It was kept by James Wardrop, Thomson's assistant and one of the museum curators.

John Thomson (1765-1846) by Andrew Geddes (1783-1844), c. 1820s. RCSEd Collections.

James Wardrop (1782-1869), John Thomson's assistant from 1807 to 1809, by Andrew Geddes. RCSEd Collections.

Formation of the museum, extract from College Minutes 5 October 1804.
'No 10. That it would greatly facilitate the teaching of surgery and prove useful as well as creditable to the College to form a Museum of morbid preparations, casts and drawings of diseases and that all the members of the College should be requested to give their assistance in promoting this very necessary part of the plan by supporting it with all such articles of this kind as may be in their power.
No 11. That this museum shall be the property of the College and be open under such regulations as the College may adopt, to the inspection of all its members.'
Photo Max McKenzie.

R. C. S. E.
GENERAL
CATALOGUE
VOL. I. No. 1–1114

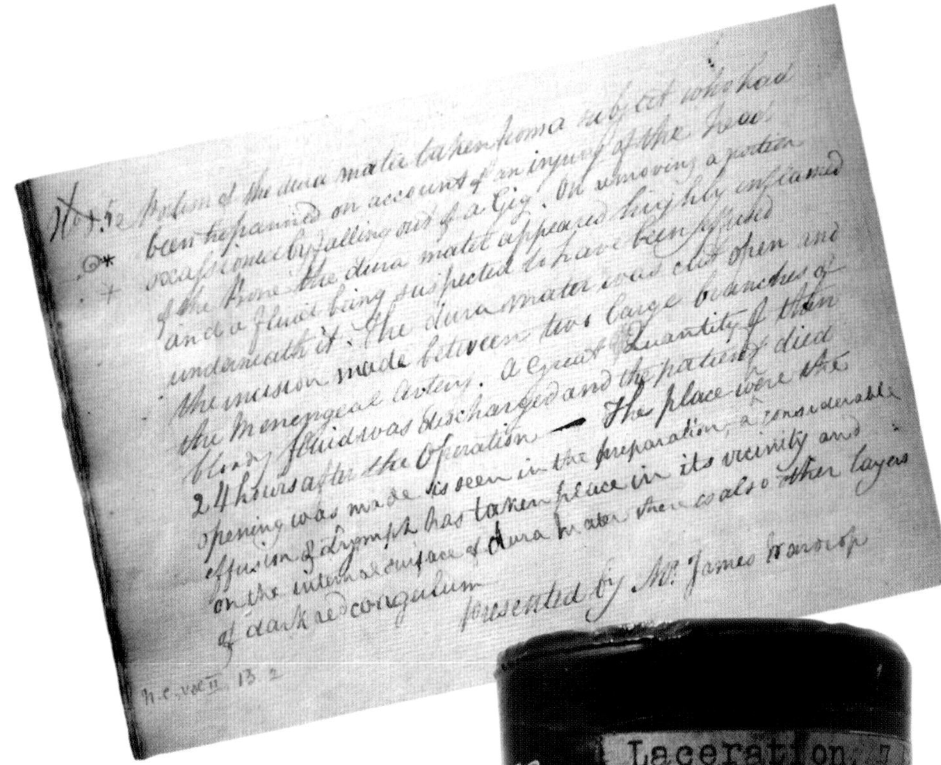

No 85 Portion of the dura mater taken from a subject who had been trepanned on account of an injury of the head occasioned by falling out of a Gig. On removing a portion of the Bone the dura mater appeared highly inflamed and a fluid being suspected to have been effused underneath it. The dura mater was cut open and the incision made between two large branches of the Menengeal Artery. A Great Quantity of thin bloody fluid was discharged and the patient died 24 hours after the Operation — The place where the opening was made is seen in the preparation, a considerable effusion of Lymph has taken place in its vicinity and on the internal surface of dura mater there is also other layers of dark red coagulum

presented by Mr James Wardrop

h.c.vol II 13.2

The first 221 entries of the General Catalogue were in the handwriting of James Wardrop. GC 85, a specimen of a lacerated wound, was also donated by him.

A portion of cerebral dura mater, showing a lacerated wound, donated by Wardop. GC 85.

The first catalogue of the Pathology Museum of the Royal College of Surgeons of Edinburgh, called the General Catalogue (GC), 1807-1825/6. RCSEd Collections.

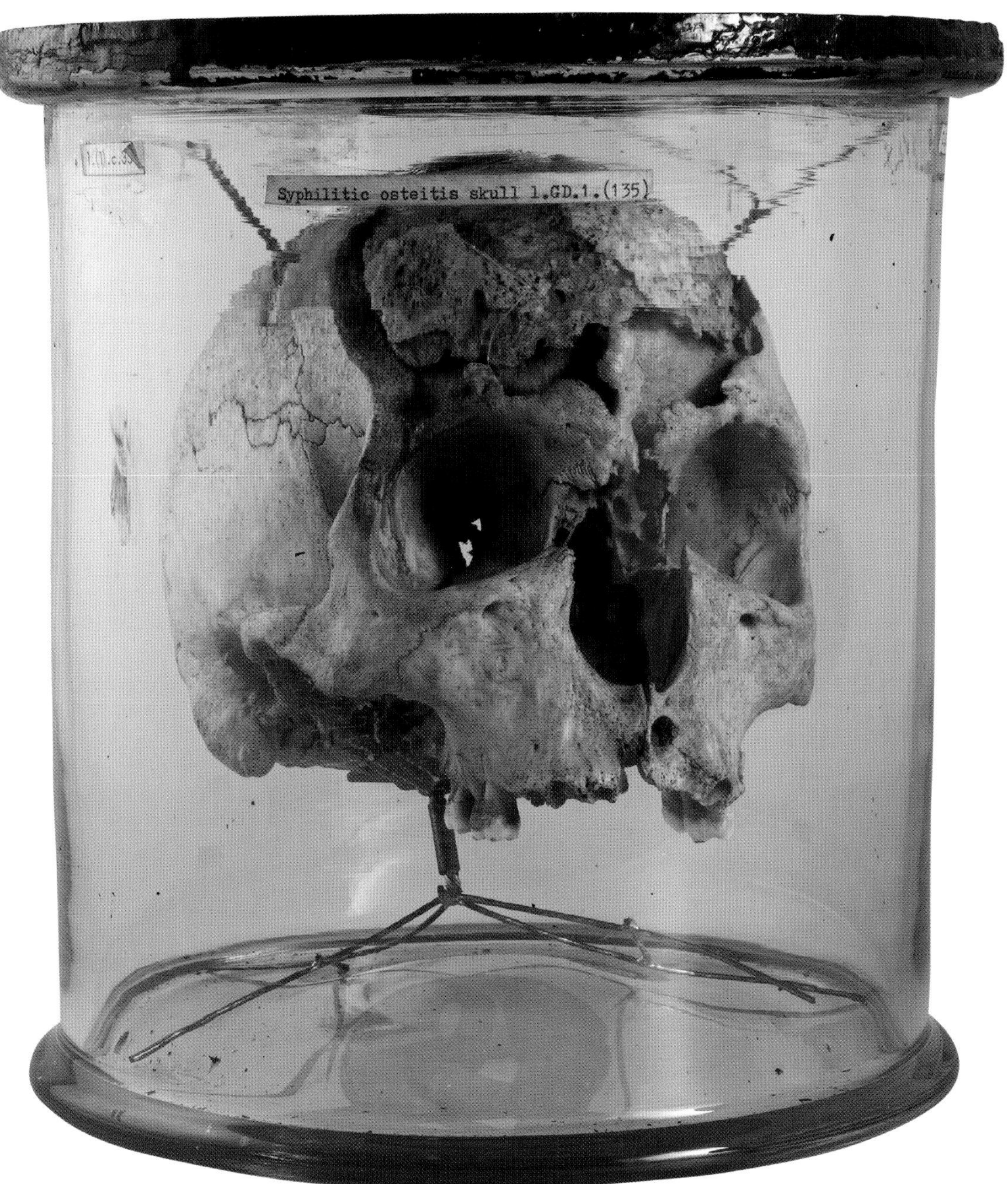

▲ **Syphilitic osteitis skull**, donated by Prof John Thomson. GC 10632.

◀ **Original Pathology Collection**
Gallery display in the Pathology Museum of specimens donated between 1804 and 1832.

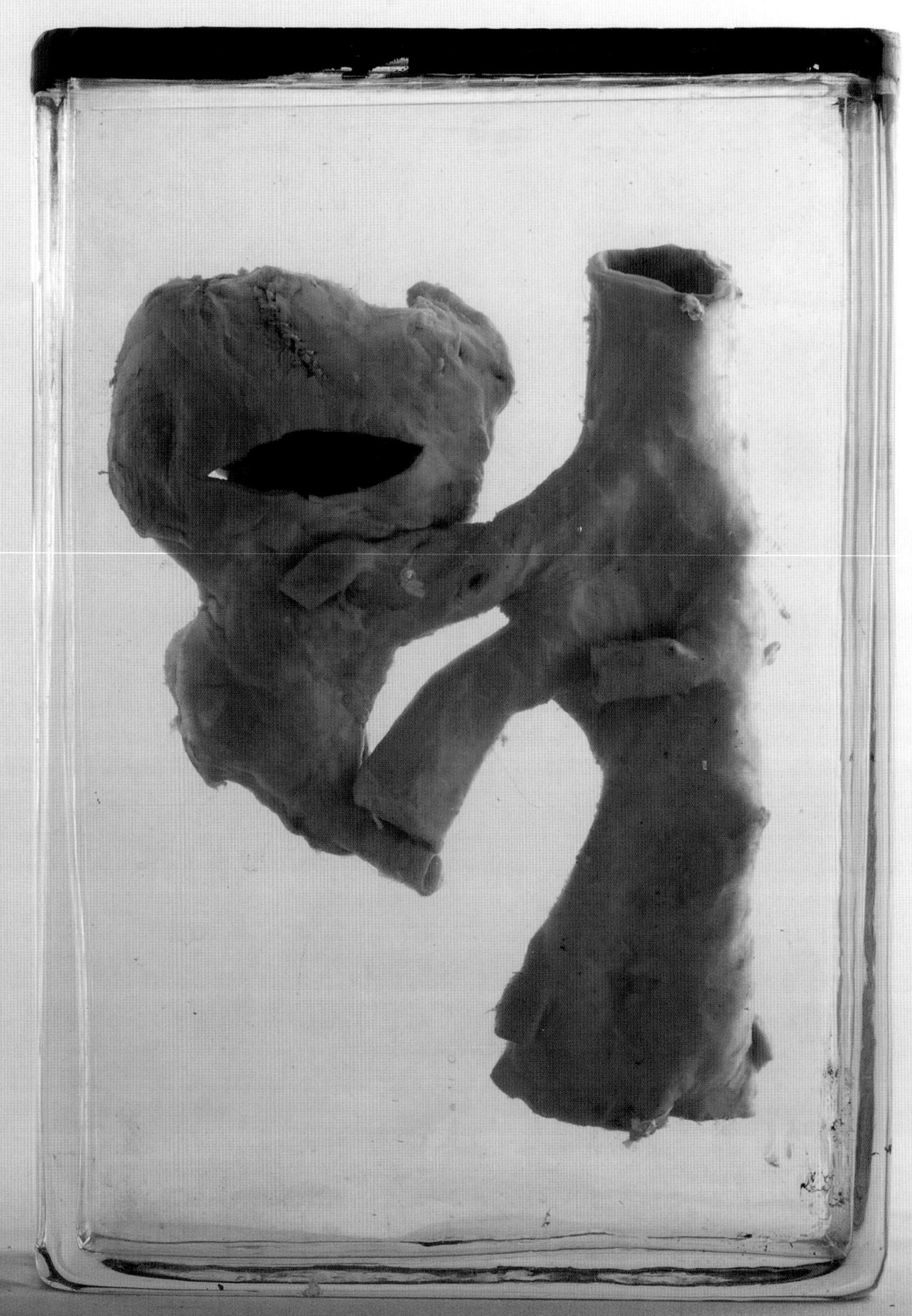

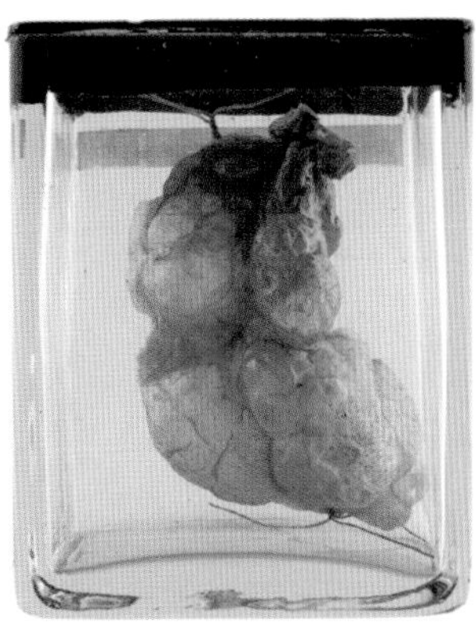

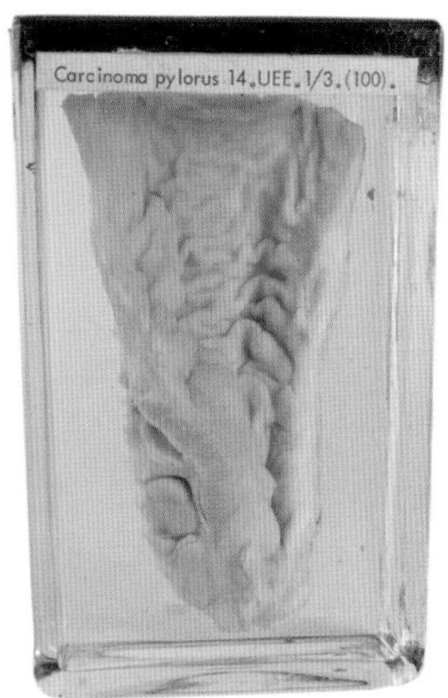

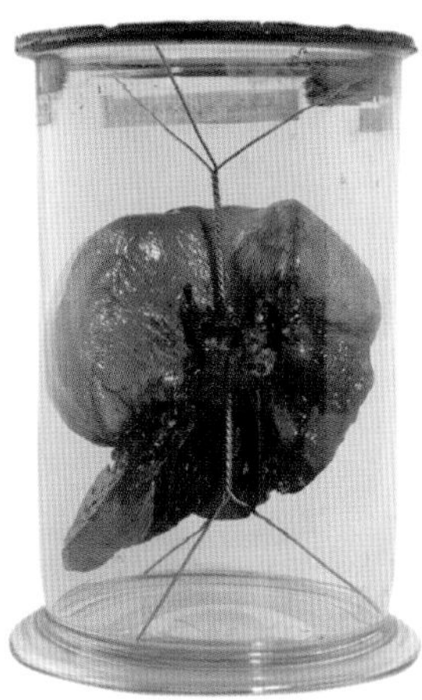

▲ LEFT TO RIGHT
The Catalogue states:
Specimen of Emphysematous lung.
The preparation is dried and varnished and is a very beautiful specimen from Dr Begbie 5 Dec 1825. GC 792.
Cancer of the Pyloriss and coats of the stomack from Dr Thomson 3 Dec. GC 479a.
Specimen of lung in a case of hopping-cough [sic]. *Dried and varnished Dr Hamilton 17 May 1825. GC 759. (It is likely that Dr Hamilton was Robert Hamilton, Keeper of the museum from 1821-26).*

◀ *Aneurysm of the Hepatic Artery*
occurring in a man of 48 who had no previous complaints. He died suddenly in bed from the rupture of the sac at the place where the whalebone is inserted. Presented by Dr Pitcairn.
The whale bone has since been removed. GC 487.

▶ *Everted and dried aortic arch.*
Specimen donated by John William Turner who was appointed as the first Keeper of the Museum in 1816. GC 237.

319.
hand.
5(9).61

Expansion

Following the end of the Napoleonic Wars in 1815 the College had built up a substantial reserve of cash, largely from income generated from the separate military and naval Diploma offered by the College during the war. By 1821, this stood 'at upwards of £9,000' and the College was keen to spend some of it on the acquisition of a suitable collection 'conducive to its own dignity as a scientific body, or to the collective and individual interest of its members.'

By the end of the decade the College owned one of Europe's most extensive and prestigious museums, incorporating the collections of two of the nineteenth century's most brilliant anatomists, and the surgeons' new Hall, designed by Scotland's leading architect William Playfair, was near completion. The decade was the most expansive in the College's history, characterised by a modernising zeal and huge financial investment. The venture however was not without some false starts.

In late 1820 the College entered negotiations with the German anatomist Frederick Meckel of Halle to buy his famed anatomy and pathology collection. The large sums of money involved reflected the College's serious intent on the development of the museum. Negotiations faltered, however, when Meckel suffered bouts of depressive illness and, while new opportunities presented themselves in Edinburgh, the sale was abandoned.

Another proposal from a William Cullen, the grand nephew of the famed physician of the same name, was also supported by the College. Cullen's plan was to spend three years in Paris acquiring specimens for the College believing that Paris would prove an easy base for such activity. He left for France in October 1822 but returned just seven weeks later his health near broken by the difficulty of his task.

◀ **Tumour of the hand, cystic sarcoma,** partly membranous and partly osseous with caries of the bones of the hand.

The written catalogue entry states: '*Removed by amputation from a young adult male. The tumour, in which there was no pulsation, was very vascular and appeared to have originated within the metacarpal bone. "The blood was contained in numerous distinct bony cysts, each of which was lined of the bones" (B.Bell. "A treatise on the disease of the bones" Edinburgh 1828. 157 and 160). Presented by Mr Joseph Bell.*' GC 319. RCSEd Collections.

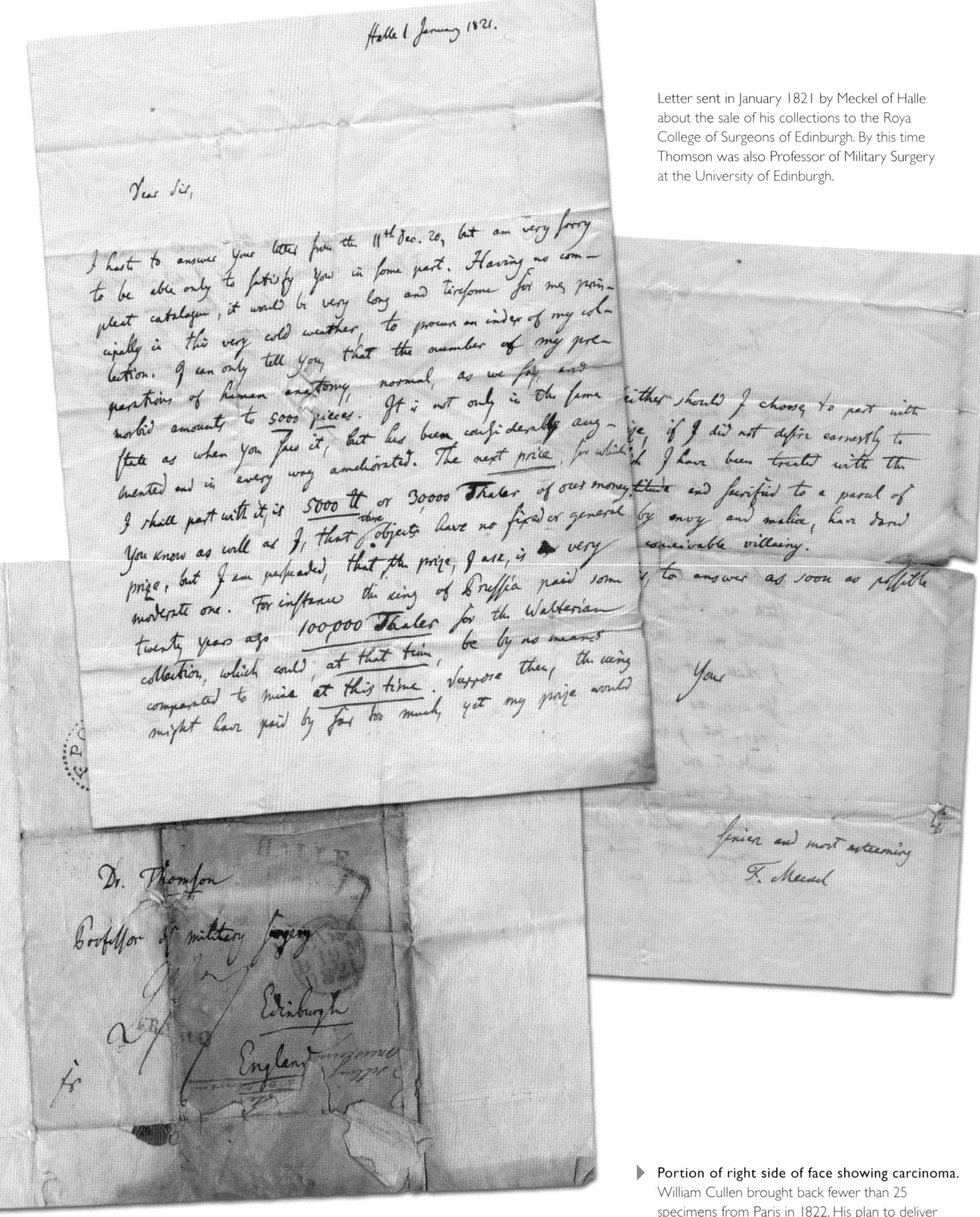

Halle 1 January 1821.

Dear Sir,

I haste to answer your letter from the 11th Dec. 20, but am very sorry to be able only to satisfy you in some part. Having no complete catalogue, it would be very long and tiresome for me principally in this very cold weather, to prepare an index of my collection. I can only tell you that the number of my preparations of human anatomy, normal, as we say, and morbid amounts to 5000 pieces. It is not only in the same state as when you saw it, but has been considerably augmented and in every way ameliorated. The next price, for which I shall part with it, is 5000 £ or 30000 Thaler of our money. You know as well as I, that above objects have no fixed or general price, but I am persuaded, that the price, I ask, is a very moderate one. For instance the King of Prussia paid some twenty years ago 100,000 Thaler for the Walterian collection, which could, at that time, be by no means compared to mine at this time. Suppose then, the King might have paid by far too much, yet my price would

…either should I chose to part with
…ce, if I did not desire earnestly to
…h I have been treated with the
…titute and sacrificed to a parcel of
…by envy and malice, have dared
…conceivable villainy.
…, to answer as soon as possible

Your

sincere and most esteeming
F. Meckel

Dr. Thomson
Professor of military Surgery
Edinburgh
England

Letter sent in January 1821 by Meckel of Halle about the sale of his collections to the Roya College of Surgeons of Edinburgh. By this time Thomson was also Professor of Military Surgery at the University of Edinburgh.

Portion of right side of face showing carcinoma. William Cullen brought back fewer than 25 specimens from Paris in 1822. His plan to deliver an extensive new anatomical collection for the College had met with failure. GC 585.

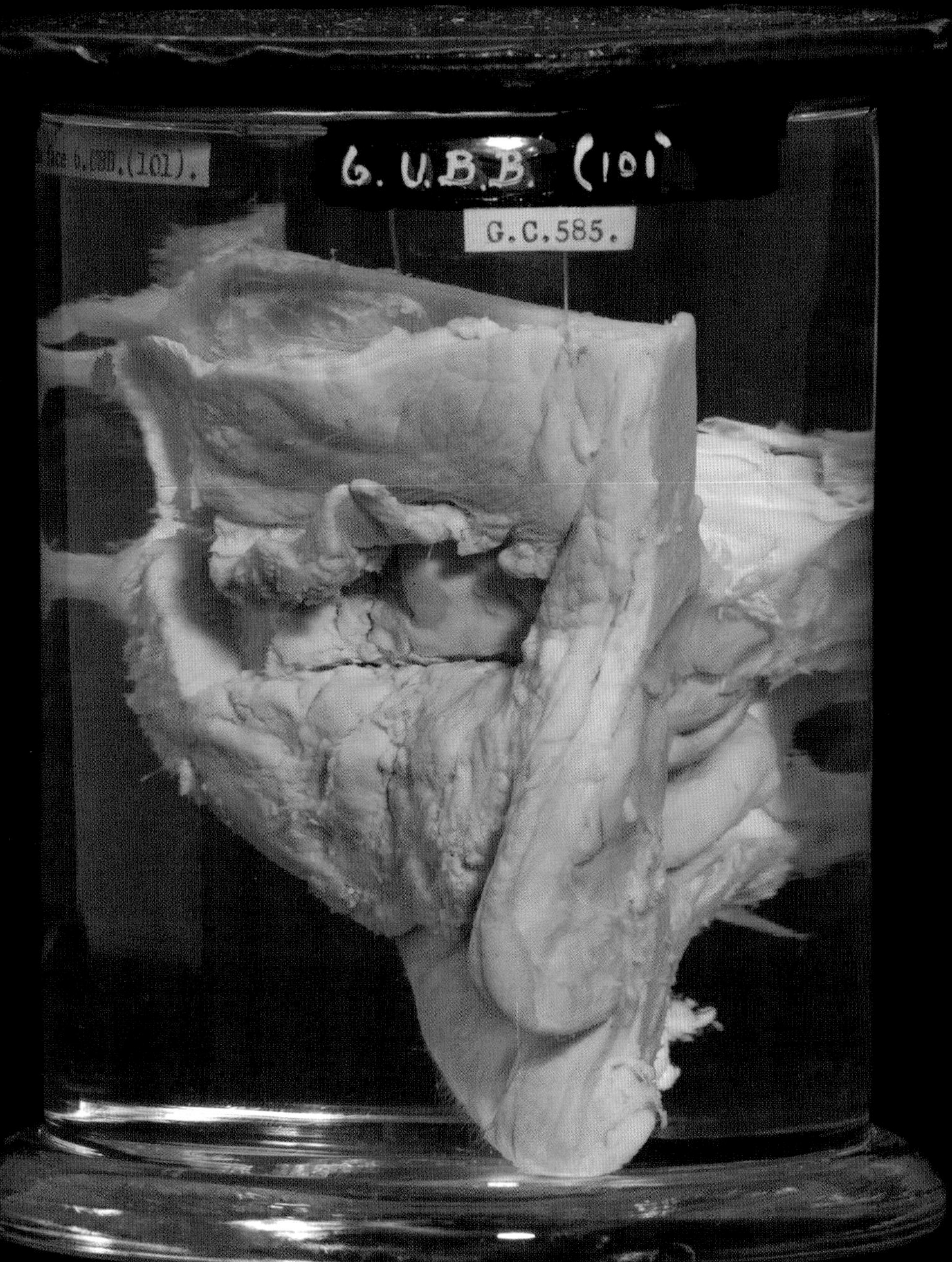
G. U.B.B. (101
G.C.585.

'All living bodies with which we are acquainted, are constructed on one general plan, possess similar, at least analogous, organs and functions; and being modified only as to class, order, genus, and species, contribute much to illustrate each other.'

John Barclay's introduction to lectures on comparative anatomy.

The Barclay Collection

The College's commitment to developing a more comprehensive museum collection came to the attention of John Barclay (1758-1826), at the time Scotland's most successful anatomy teacher and one of the most revered in Europe.

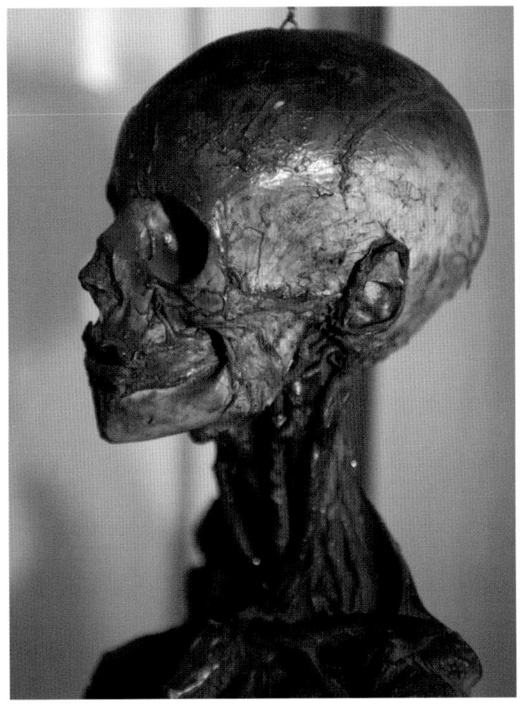

Barclay had developed a particular interest and expertise in comparative anatomy and had amassed an impressive teaching collection of over 2,500 specimens, many of them large mammals, including the skeleton of an Indian elephant.

The College's interest in securing Meckel's collection provided Barclay with a solution to the long term housing of his own museum. In July 1821 Barclay offered his collection to the College on certain conditions, including that a hall suitable for its display should be built.

Most of Barclay's collection of comparative anatomy survived at Surgeons' Hall until the 1950s, but by that time its marginal relevance to the teaching of human pathology led to its disposal or transfer to other natural history collections. Only an elephant skull, three human skeletons and a few other specimens were kept.

▲ **Human dissection by John Barclay.** In 1876 the skeletons in the Barclay Collections were 'varnished over with turpentine to remove and prevent growth of mould,' *Museum Minute Book* 1859-1880. RCSEd Collections.

◀ **Bust of John Barclay** by Samuel Joseph. The bust was paid for by Barclay's students, testimony to his popularity and gift for teaching. RCSEd Collections.

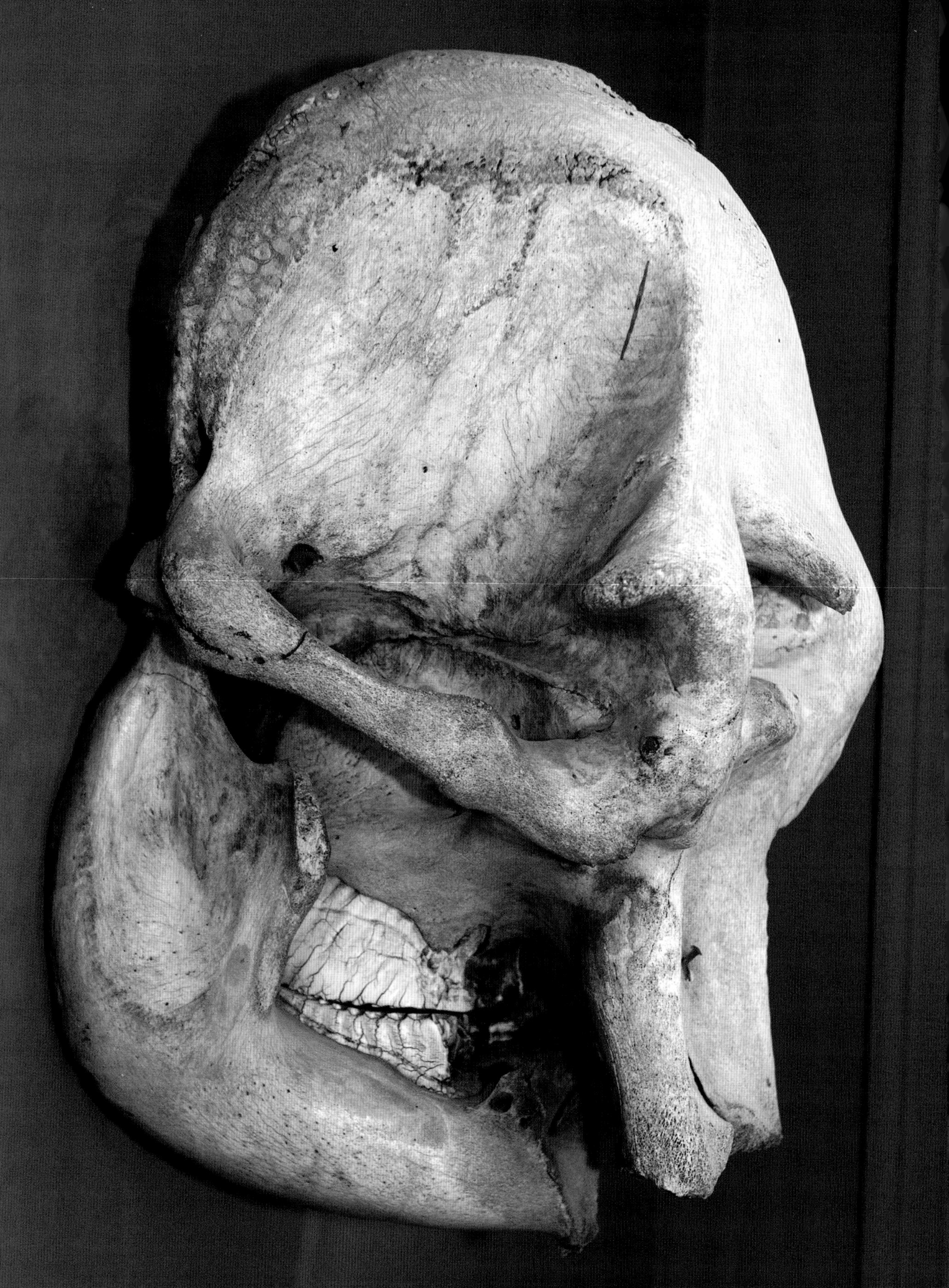

The Craft in Danger

In 1817 John Barclay was the most likely candidate for a new Professorship of Comparative Anatomy at Edinburgh University, however the post was viewed as a threat by existing professors, likely concerned that Barclay's popularity as a teacher would impact on their income and influence. John Kay's print *The Craft in Danger* shows Barclay riding the skeleton of an elephant into the University College while James Gregory, Alexander Monro *tertius*, Thomas Hope and Robert Jameson, the Professors of Medicine; Anatomy; Chemistry and Natural History respectively are shown opposing his entry. The accompanying text to the print in John Kay's *Originals* published in 1837-8, notes:

'The skeleton of the elephant was prepared by Sir George Ballingall while serving as assistant-surgeon with the second battalion of the Royals in India; was subsequently presented by him to his old master, Dr Barclay; and ultimately bequeathed by the Doctor, along with the rest of his collection, to the Royal College of Surgeons, in whose valuable Museum it forms a conspicuous object.'

▲ *The Craft in Danger* by John Kay, first printed in *Kay's Originals*, 1837. Private Collection.

◀ **The skull of the Indian elephant** from John Barclay's original collection of comparative anatomy, given to him by George Ballingall, later President of the Royal College of Surgeons of Edinburgh. RCSEd Collections.

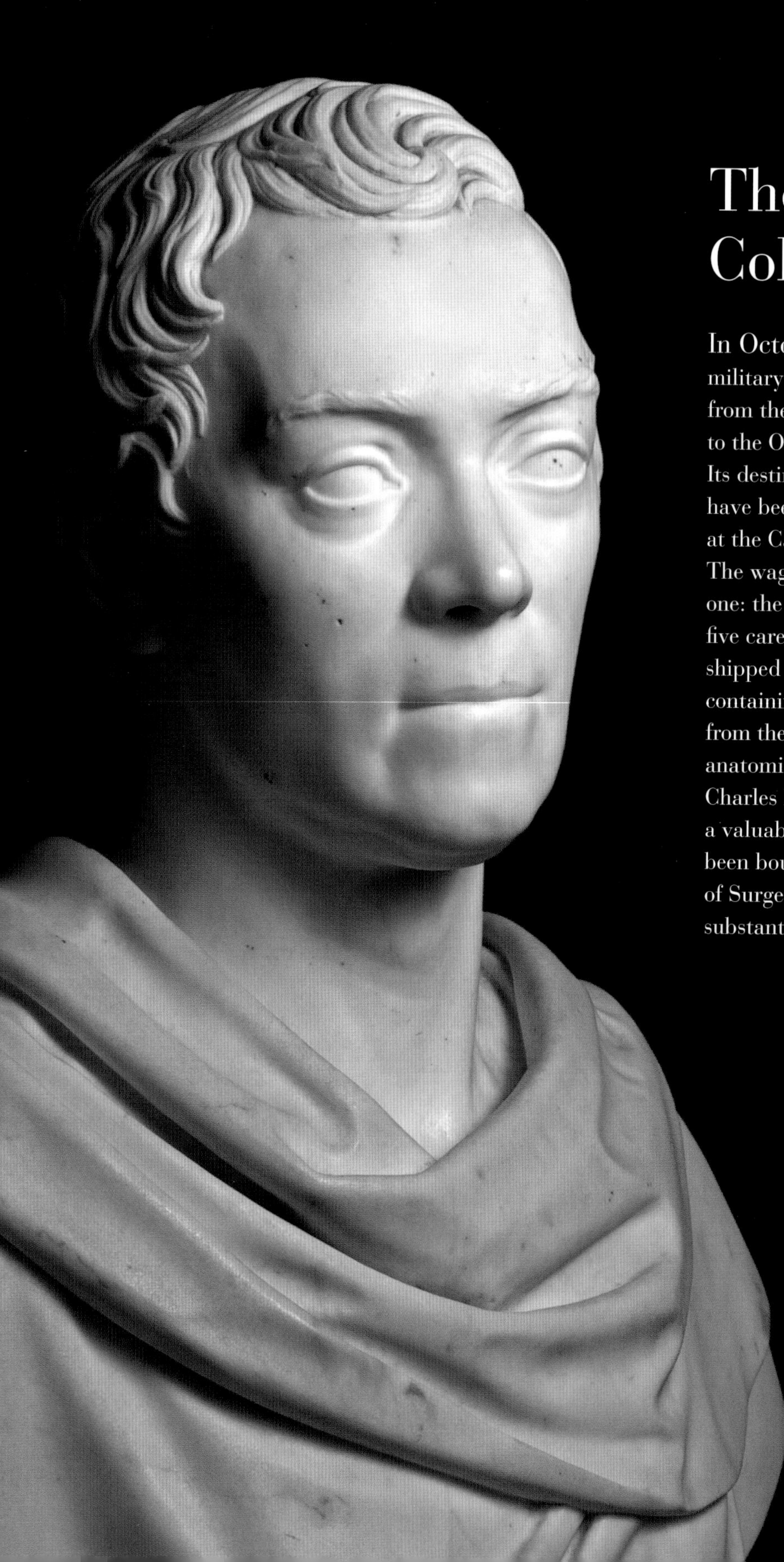

The Bell Collection

In October 1825 a convoy of military wagons made its way from the dockside at Leith up on to the Old Town of Edinburgh. Its destination was not, as might have been supposed, the garrison at the Castle but Surgeons' Hall. The wagons' cargo was a peculiar one: the first consignment of sixty five carefully packed crates, shipped by sea from London, containing around 3,000 exhibits from the museum of the renowned anatomist, surgeon and teacher Charles Bell. The cargo was also a valuable one having recently been bought by the Royal College of Surgeons of Edinburgh for the substantial sum of £3,000.

Charles Bell was born in Edinburgh in 1774. He was apprenticed to his surgeon brother John (1763-1820) in 1792, working alongside him at his anatomy school in Edinburgh's Surgeon Square. In 1799 Charles qualified as a Fellow of the Royal College of Surgeons of Edinburgh and took over the formal teaching at the school.

However Edinburgh offered few opportunities for Charles to progress in either surgery or anatomy. Although his brother was one of Scotland's most successful surgeons he had made enemies in Edinburgh's medical establishment and Charles, by association, had no prospect of being given either a university or Royal Infirmary appointment.

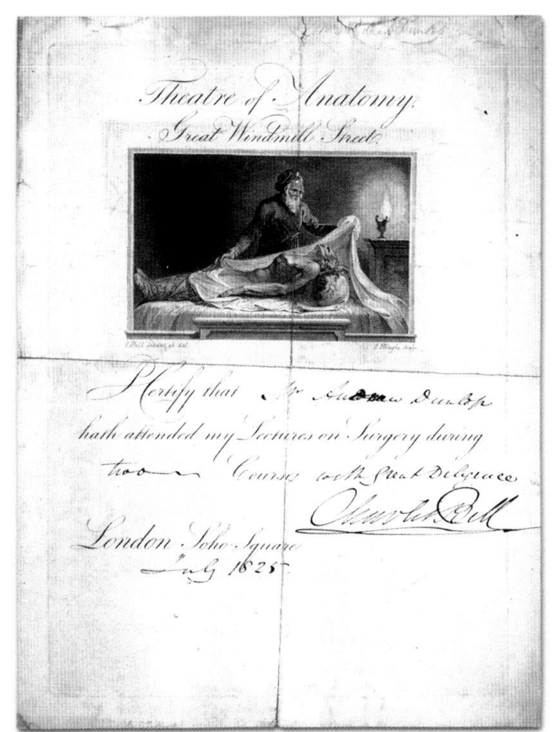

Theatre of Anatomy.
Great Windmill Street.

I Certify that Mr Andrew Dunlop
hath attended my Lectures on Surgery during
two Courses with great Diligence
Charles Bell
London Soho Square
Aug 1825

▲ **Certificate of attendance, Charles Bell's Great Windmill Street Anatomy School, London, 1825.** The engraving is by John Bell from *The Principles of Surgery*, Vol. II, Part II, 1806. RCSEd Collections.

Charles moved to London in 1804 and immediately set to work on making a new collection of anatomical and pathological specimens. In the same year John Bell gave up his school and much of the Edinburgh collection was shipped down to Charles in London.

In 1812 Charles bought the Great Windmill Street Anatomy School in London from James Wilson. Two years later he was appointed as a surgeon to the Middlesex Hospital and went on to found the Medical School there. Much of the development of the collection was then carried out by his brother-in-law, John Shaw.

Bell's most important work was on the nervous system and he was the first to identify that the anterior and posterior spinal nerve roots had different functions.

In 1825 Shaw was also appointed to the surgical staff of the Middlesex Hospital and Bell decided to sell the Great Windmill Street School and his collections. Bell returned to Edinburgh in 1836 when he was appointed Professor of Surgery at the University.

◀ **Charles Bell** (1774-1842). Bust in marble by William Theed, 1851. RCSEd Collections.

EX LIBRIS
BIBLIOTH.
COLLEGII REGII
CHIRURG.
EDINENSIS.
Bell Collection
printed catalogue
London 1819

Introduction to the printed catalogue of the Bell Collection of the Great Windmill Street School of Anatomy, London 1819.

'The formation of this Museum, may be divided into three periods, – that formed by Mr. Wilson, that formed by Mr. Bell, and the addition made during the last seven years.

Mr. Bell's original Collection consisted of preparations, both of Natural and Morbid Anatomy. It was particularly valuable in Quicksilver Preparations; in Preparations of the Lymphatics; in Diseased Bones; in Diseases of the Bladder and Urethra, and in Models of Diseased Viscera.

The Collection of Mr. Wilson was remarkable for the exquisitely neat manner in which the Preparations had been dissected and preserved. Its value was principally in the complete Series of Preparations, exhibiting the Minute Structure, and arranged so as to correspond with the Lectures. These must always form an important part of the Present Museum from their intrinsic value, as well as from the Maker, who learned his art under the celebrated Mr. Cruickshank (the fine Collection of Mr Cruickshank was bought by the Empress of Russia), the Colleague of Dr. Hunter.

By the arrangement betwixt Mr. Wilson and Mr. Bell, Mr. Wilson's Preparations became the property of the latter, and the two Collections were united. Since that period, that is in the last seven years, great additions have been made (not less than one third of the whole). To the pupils of that period, it is not necessary to say that this has been done principally through the labours of Mr. Shaw. Mr. Shaw was a pupil of Mr. Bell's at a very early age, and has continued making Preparations under him for eleven years.'

Cover of the first printed catalogue of the Bell Collection of the Great Windmill Street School of Anatomy, London, 1819. RCSEd Collections.

'I do not know what puts it in my head that Wilson would like to make a connection with me. I have had some conversation with him to-day. Wilson, you know, is second in descent from Dr Hunter in the school of Great Windmill Street'

CHARLES BELL letter to his brother, sent from London on 30 November 1804.

A. Blood — page 1.
B. Heart — 3 & 402.
C. Arteries — 13. | +.C. Arteries dry preparations
D. Veins — 25. | +.D. Veins dry preparations of
E. Absorbents — 29.
F. Bone — 31. | +.F. Bones D°. D°
G. Diseases of Bone — 50. | +.G. Bones diseases of not in bottles
H. Joints — 67. | +.H. Joints diseased not in bottles.
I. Cellular & Adipose Membrane 89. | +.F. continued
J. Muscle — 91.
K. Teeth — 96
L. Brain and Nerves — 131 & 433. 2/.
M. Eye — 139.
N. Ear — 163.
O. Mouth — 187.
P. Nose — 195.
Q. Skin — 206.
R. Larynx, Trachea &c 220.
S. Lungs — 231.
T. Female Breast — 239.
U. Pharynx, Oesophagus &c. 243.
V. Stomach — 247. & 407 & 423
W. Small Intestines Structure of. 257.
X. D°. Diseases of — 271. & 409
Y. Great Intestines Structure of — 287.
Z. D°. D° Diseases of. — 294.
AA. Liver — 301.
BB. D°. Diseases of — 306. & 416
CC. Pancreas — 316.
DD. Spleen — 318.
EE. Kidney Structure of 321.
FF. D°. Diseases of — 329.
GG. Calculi — 333.
HH. Bladder — 339.
II. Penis — 351.
JJ. Testes — 363.
KK. Vagina Uterus &c — 371.
LL. Diseases of D° — 381 & 418
MM. Gravid Uterus — 389
NN. D°. Comparative — 399

A Catalogue of the Anatomical Preparations belonging to James Wilson of Great Windmill Street — all not otherwise marked were made by himself — & intended to supply the loss of the collection of the late Doctor William Hunter —

The Letters in the 1st Column shew the class the Preparations belong to — the figures in the same column their arrangement in that class.

The Letters in the 2nd Column express how the Preparation is preserved. viz — S. means in British Spirits. T. means in Spirit of Turpentine. V means Varnished. D. means Dry.

Doctor Hunters Collection left England in September 1807

This Catalogue was finished in November 1808.

The date of the year in which most of the preparations were made or came into his possession is added to the description.

The Letter A is placed in the press on the side of the Staircase nearest to the Dwelling house — NN. on the side of the staircase nearest to the Theatre

Title page of the Catalogue of the Collections of James Wilson. In 1812 Charles Bell bought the Great Windmill Street Anatomy School and its collection from Wilson. This catalogue was presented to the College by Wilson's family in 1828.

Enteric Fever, Wilson Collection, a specimen showing the effects of enteric fever on the small intestine. Mounted on its original wooden stand, WC X33. GC 10935. RCSEd Collections.

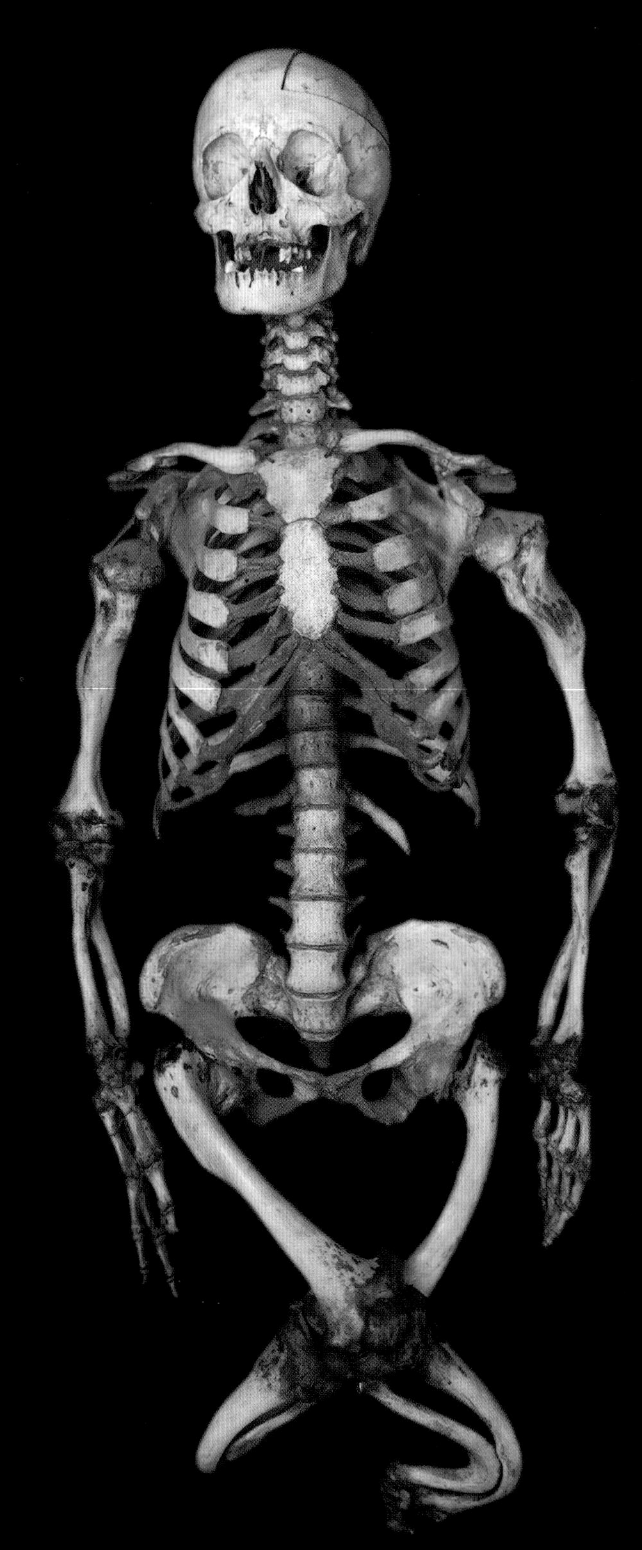

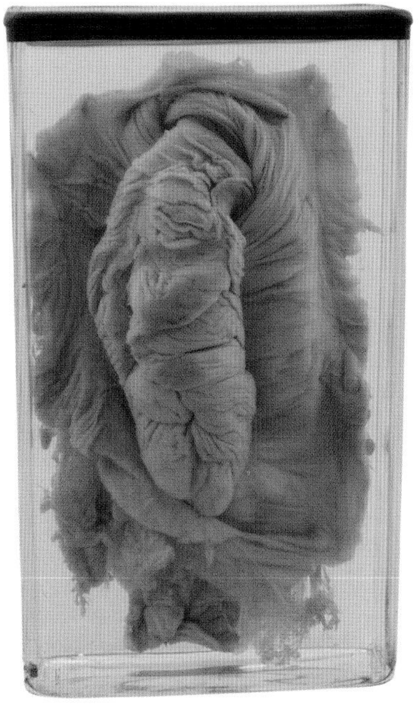

'I have found out that I can model in clay, and work it up as my base without casting in plaster of Paris, which is a great facility to me, and saving of expense.'

CHARLES BELL letter to his brother, 6 June 1805.

Specimen of colon. BC xiii.4.M.I.5, GC 10923.

Plaster and wax model made by Charles Bell, c.1800 of the specimen shown above. BC xiii.4.M.I.6, GC 10923.

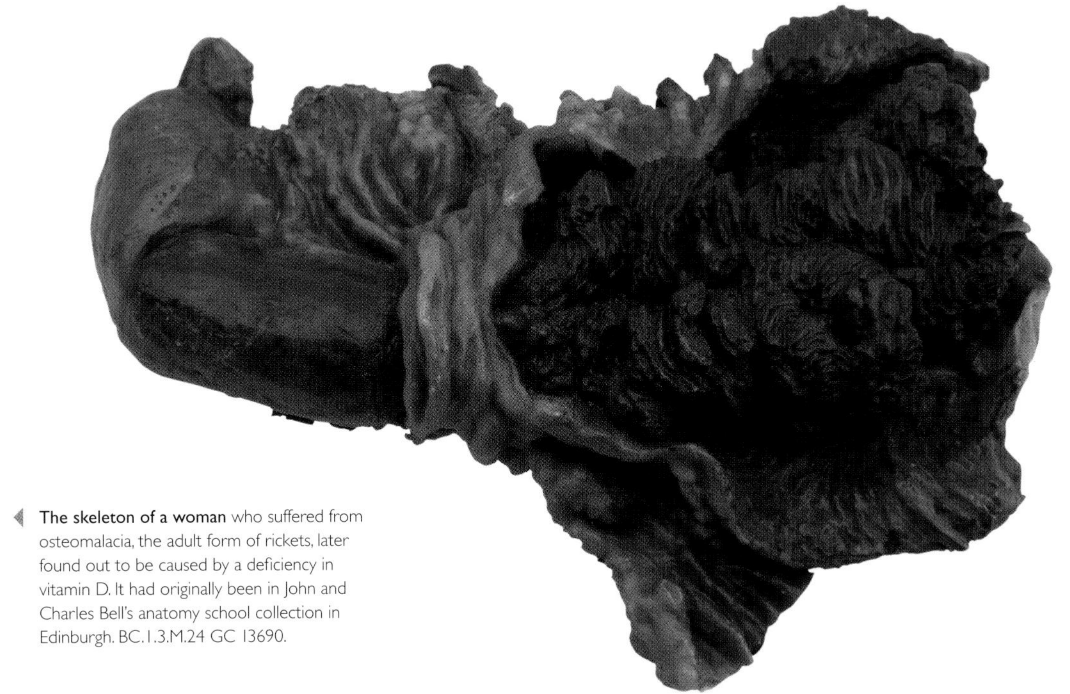

The skeleton of a woman who suffered from osteomalacia, the adult form of rickets, later found out to be caused by a deficiency in vitamin D. It had originally been in John and Charles Bell's anatomy school collection in Edinburgh. BC.1.3.M.24 GC 13690.

'My two cases are already filled with preparations, newly varnished, with papers behind the glass.'... 'I shall soon be universally known, and my museum will increase rapidly.'

CHARLES BELL, letters to his brother from London, 28 October 1805 and 4 February 1806.

Enteric lymph vessels injected with mercury. BC, xii.5.N.5. GC 12604.

Heart and Lungs. BC, xi.2.N.4 GC 12893.

Abdominal aorta mounted on paper. BC, v.2.N.17 GC 12764.

Spine. BC, I.N.73 GC 12395.

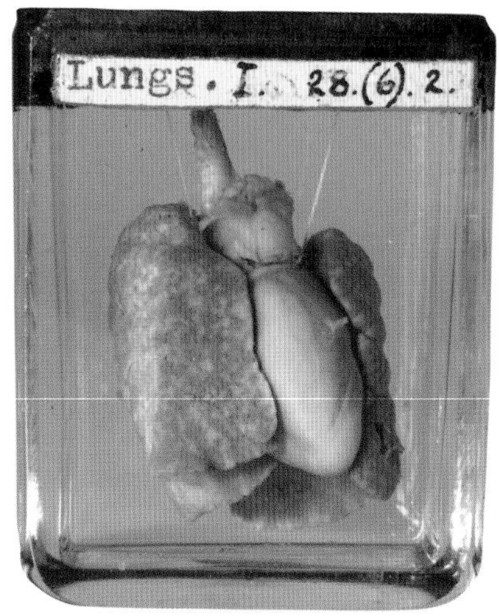

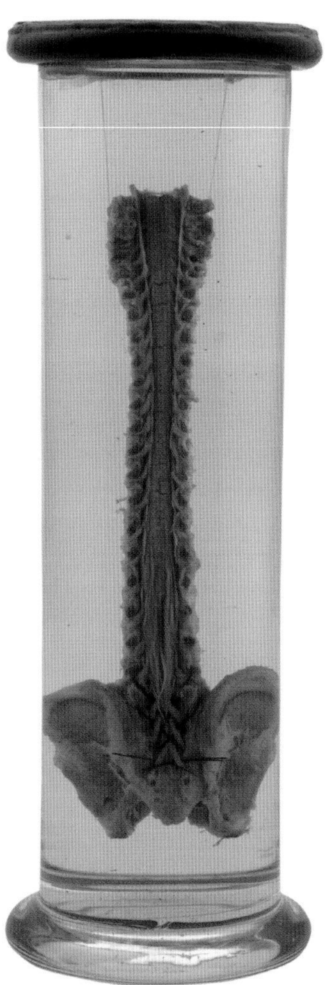

Enteric lymph vessels. 26.(2).6.

◀ **Bell catalogue entry:**
'An aneurism of the descending Thoracic Aorta, the Patient lay long in the Middlesex Hospital being kept very low, and occasionally bled, his sufferings were by no means so acute, as we would imagine must necessarily result from such extensive disease, and not nearly so much as we find in Patients who having affections of the Heart, afford no morbid appearance on dissection: the Tumour has burst through to the back part, where it formed a very large Tumour during life, notwithstanding the distance of this posterior sac, from the Heart, the pulsation of the Tumour was at all Times very distinct: though we learn that such Anuerisms have been mistaken for chronic Abcess, he died exhausted from weakness.'
B.C.xii.2.M.57. GC 11006.

▶ **Bell catalogue entry:**
'Aorta having an Aneurism at the place of the coeliac arteries, distended and dried from a Woman about forty five years of age who was a patient in the Middlesex Hospital, and was treated for a complaint in her Uterus, no blood was found effused. There are specks of ossific concretion near the Situation of the rupture of the Artery. The Womb was extensively diseased.'
B.C. xii.2M.56. GC 11012.

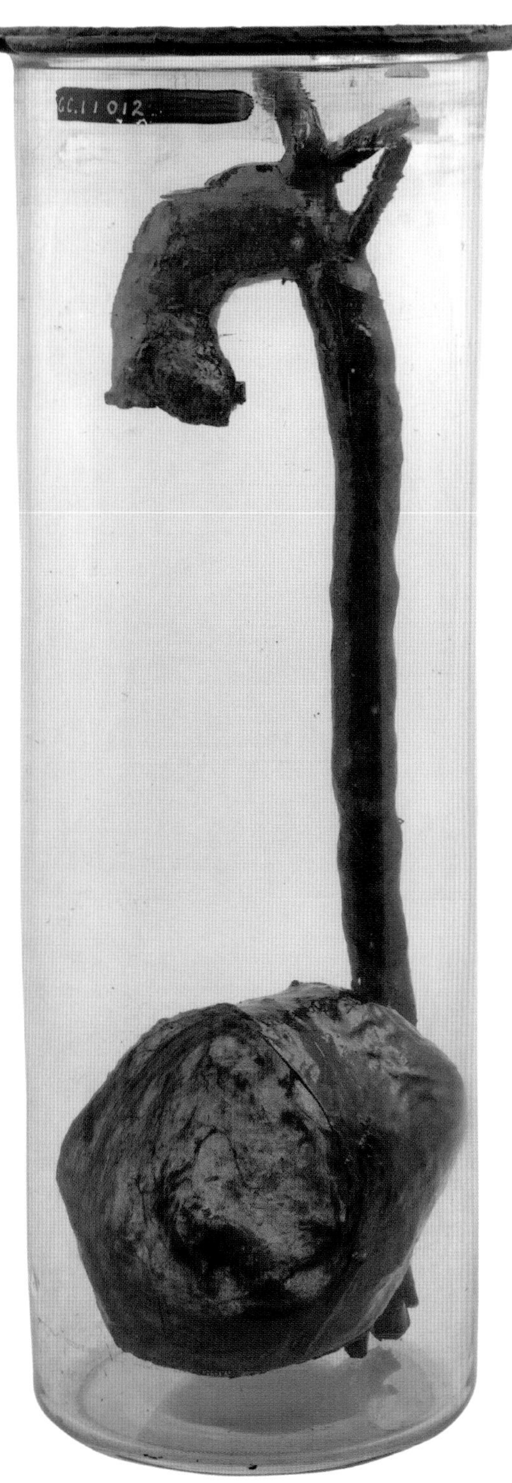

The Art of Charles Bell

Charles Bell's talents as an anatomist and teacher were greatly enhanced by his artistic skill. His first published works had been in collaboration with his brother John, illustrating John's *Engravings explaining the anatomy of the Bones, Muscles and Joints* in 1794 and co-authoring and illustrating *The Anatomy of the Human Body* Vols 1 & 2 in 1797.

For the rest of his life Bell was to illustrate his own works with drawings and engravings of exceptional quality, most notably: *A System of Dissections, explaining the anatomy of the human body* (1798); *The Anatomy of the Brain* (1802); *Essays on the Anatomy of Expression in Painting* (1806); *Illustrations of the Great Operations of Surgery* (1821), and *The Hand, its Mechanism and Vital Endowments, as Evincing Design* (1833).

Charles Bell, *Illustrations of the Great Operations of Surgery. Trepan, Hernia, Amputation, Aneurism and Lithotomy* (1821), Plate IX. The plate shows the method used for leg amputation at the thigh. RCSEd Collections.

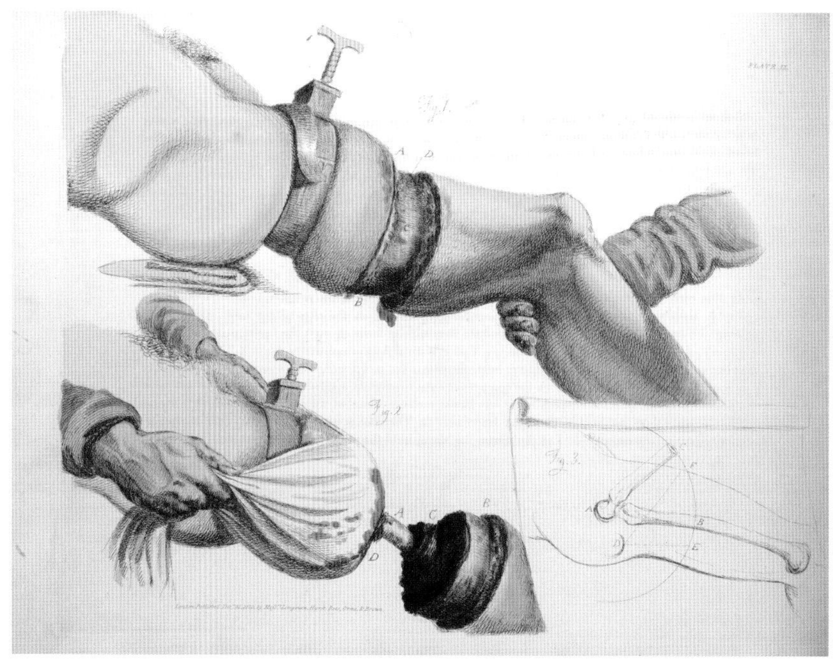

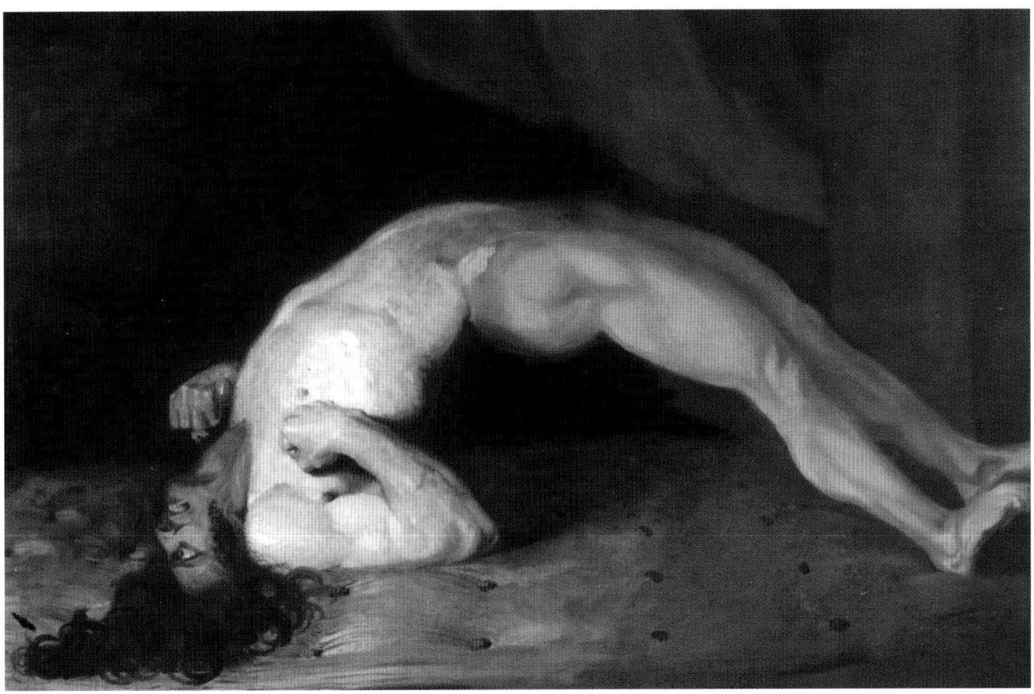

Opisthotonus by Charles Bell, 1809.
Bell catalogue entry: '*Tetanus following gunshot wounds. Sketch in oil of opisthotonus taken from three soldiers, who were wounded at Corunna, and brought to Portsmouth.*' Opisthotonus is caused by spasm of the muscles of the back in the final stages of tetanus.
RCSEd Collections. GC 1.38.42.

Bell's artistic abilities were to serve him well when he undertook duties at the Haslar naval hospital in Portsmouth in 1809, treating casualties of the Battle of Corunna.

Bell brought back from Portsmouth 'some noble specimens of injured bones, and series of cases admirably suited for lectures,' plus a sketchbook filled with illustrations of many of the cases he had either operated on or observed. He was later to work these sketches up into 15 large oil paintings and a series of engravings to illustrate his published work on gunshot wounds.

These oil paintings provide a rare insight into the early nineteenth century world, both of warfare and surgery. In a world before X-rays, as a precise and objective record of specific cases, the paintings were intended to help surgeons visualise, by careful external observation of the patient what might be happening inside their body. Seen away from this surgical context, the paintings are a stark reminder of the universal realities of war and the trials of a soldier's life. The Corunna oils form one of the most important elements of the Bell Collection.

▲ **Painting in oil by Charles Bell**, RCSEd Collections. B.C.xvii.25. Bell catalogue entry:
Gunshot wound of the humerus. *'In this sketch in oil the apparently trifling nature of the wound, is represented. Through such a wound however the finger can be introduced, and if the bone be shattered, as in this instance, jagged points of the fragments will be felt, all around. The observation made to me on this very case was to this effect, when I feel the bone broken merely I do not amputate, but when I feel it thus, the finger passing through the bone, this is the case for amputation.'*

▼ **Humerus amputated from the wounded soldier pictured above.** B.C. xvii.24. GC 13830.

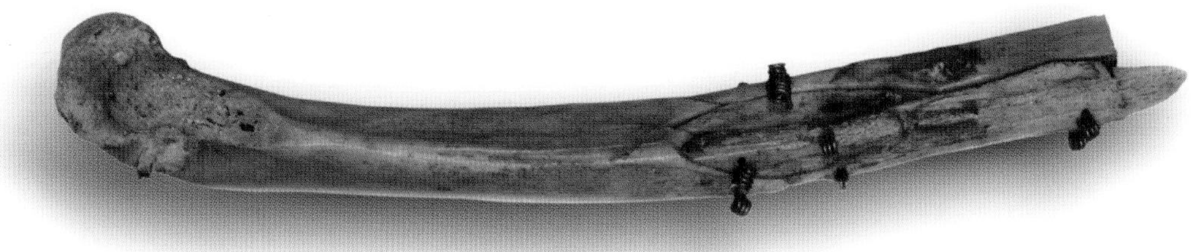

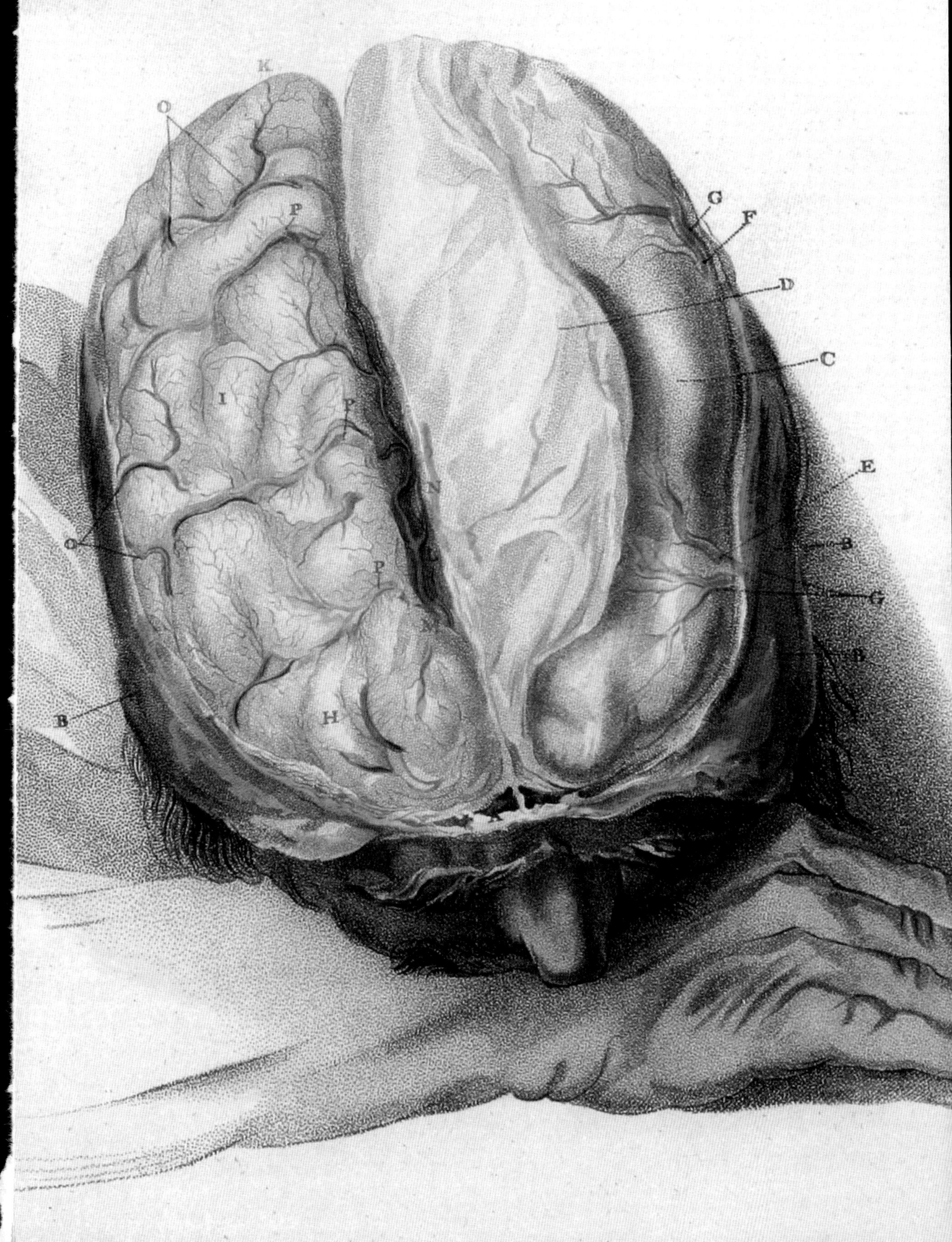
K
O
P
G
F
D
C
I
P
N
E
O
B
P
G
B
B
H

Gunshot fracture of the scapula.
BC xvii.17 GC 13829.

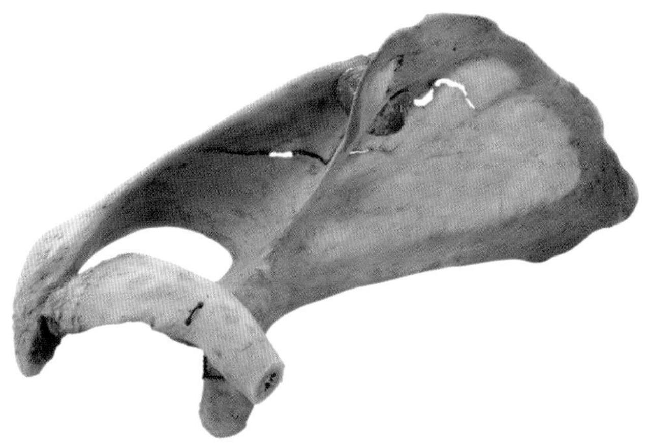

Painting in oil by Charles Bell,
RCSEd Collections. GC 13844. Bell catalogue entry:
'*Gunshot wound of the clavicle and scapula*'.
The musket ball is lodged in the back of the scapula this I took from the body of Capt…the ball entered in the breast, broke the end of the clavicle, entered the chest, and went across the lungs, broke a rib on the back part, stuck in the scapula the spent ball being nearly divided in two by the spine of the scapula; I was present when he was brought ashore in Portsmouth, in a very exhausted condition, and labouring in his breathing, he died the next day, which was the twelfth from receiving the wound. On opening the body I was astonished at finding the quantity of serum, which poured out from the chest, as out of a barrel, the lungs were condensed and gorged with blood, he could have been much relieved by the operation of paracentesis.'
Operative Surgery, 2nd Edition.'

'The musket ball is lodged in the back of the scapula this I took from the body.'
CHARLES BELL

'... I am going to establish my Anatomy of the Brain on facts the most important that have been discovered in the history of the science ... I have entertained the idea that the parts of the brain were distinct in function, and that the cerebrum was in a particular manner the organ of mind... Taking these facts as they stand, is it not most curious that there should be thus established a distinction in the parts of a nerve, and that a nerve should be insensible.'

Charles Bell, letter to his brother, 12 March 1810.

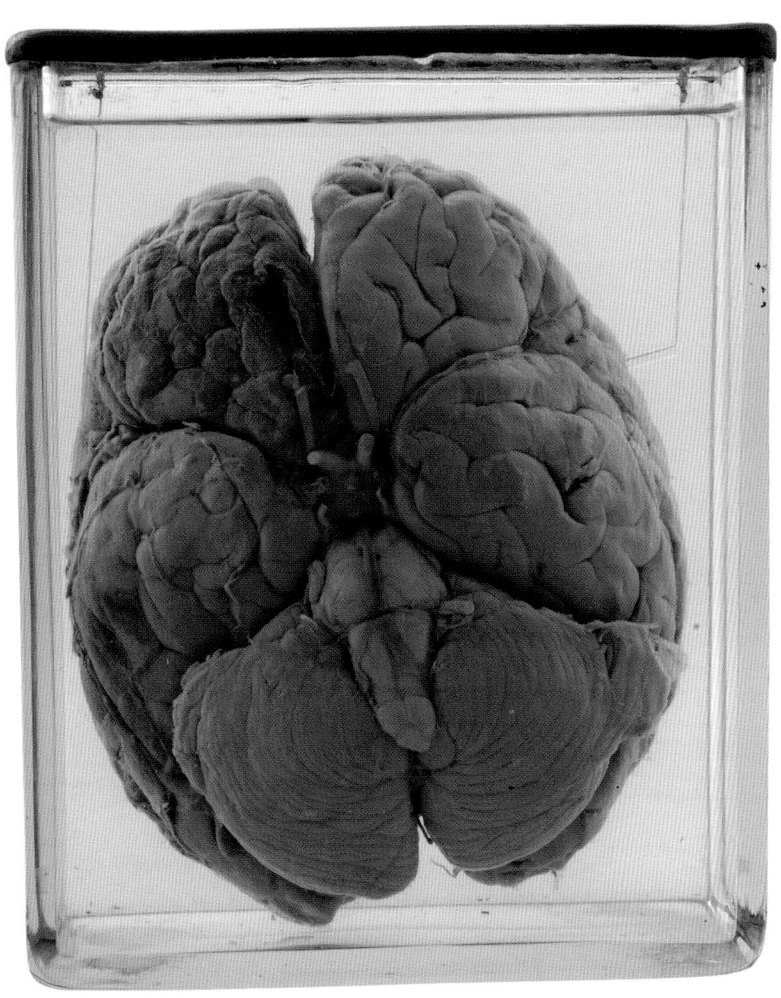

Human Brain. GC 13829. RCSEd Collections.

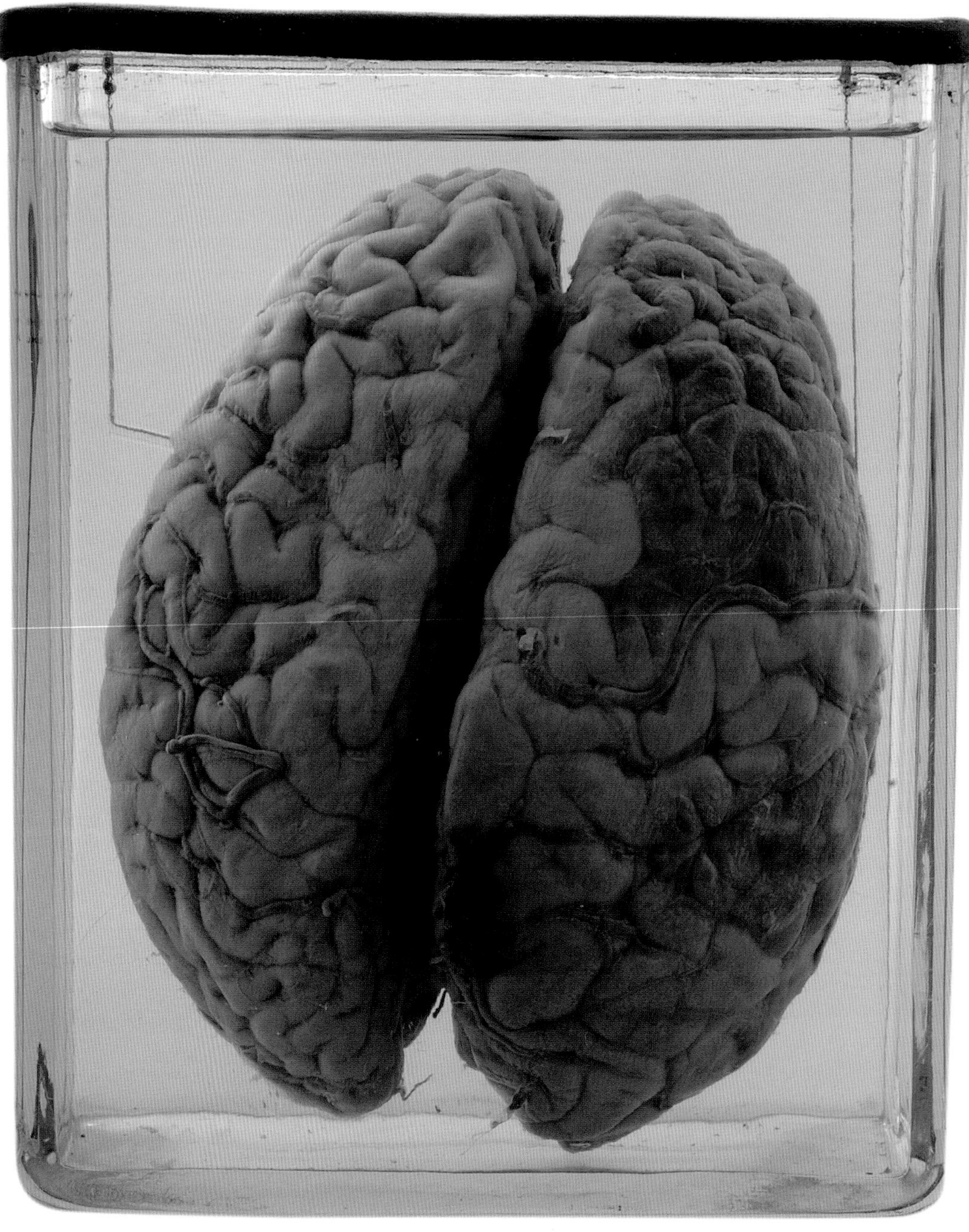

Bell had written an important work on the *Anatomy of the Brain* in 1802. His letter of 12 March 1810 is especially important as it records the date of Bell's first series of experiments on the roots of the spinal nerves.

Bell's most important discoveries in anatomy were connected to the nervous system. He identified that the anterior and posterior spinal nerve roots differed in function and that different nerves linked specific areas of the brain to peripheral parts of the body.

Human brain from above after removal of skull. *Anatomy of the Brain*, Charles Bell, 1802. RCSEd Collections.

Cranial nerves B.C. v.2.N.1. GC 12580.

'This business of the nerves will be long of coming forward exactly as it should be, but my own has a rest in this, that I have made a greater discovery than ever was made by any one man in anatomy...' CHARLES BELL letter, early 1821.

His pioneering work in this area is remembered through the Bell-Magendie Rule which is used in anatomy to indicate the direction of conduction in the spinal nerve roots. He also described the condition of facial paralysis, named after him, Bell's Palsy.

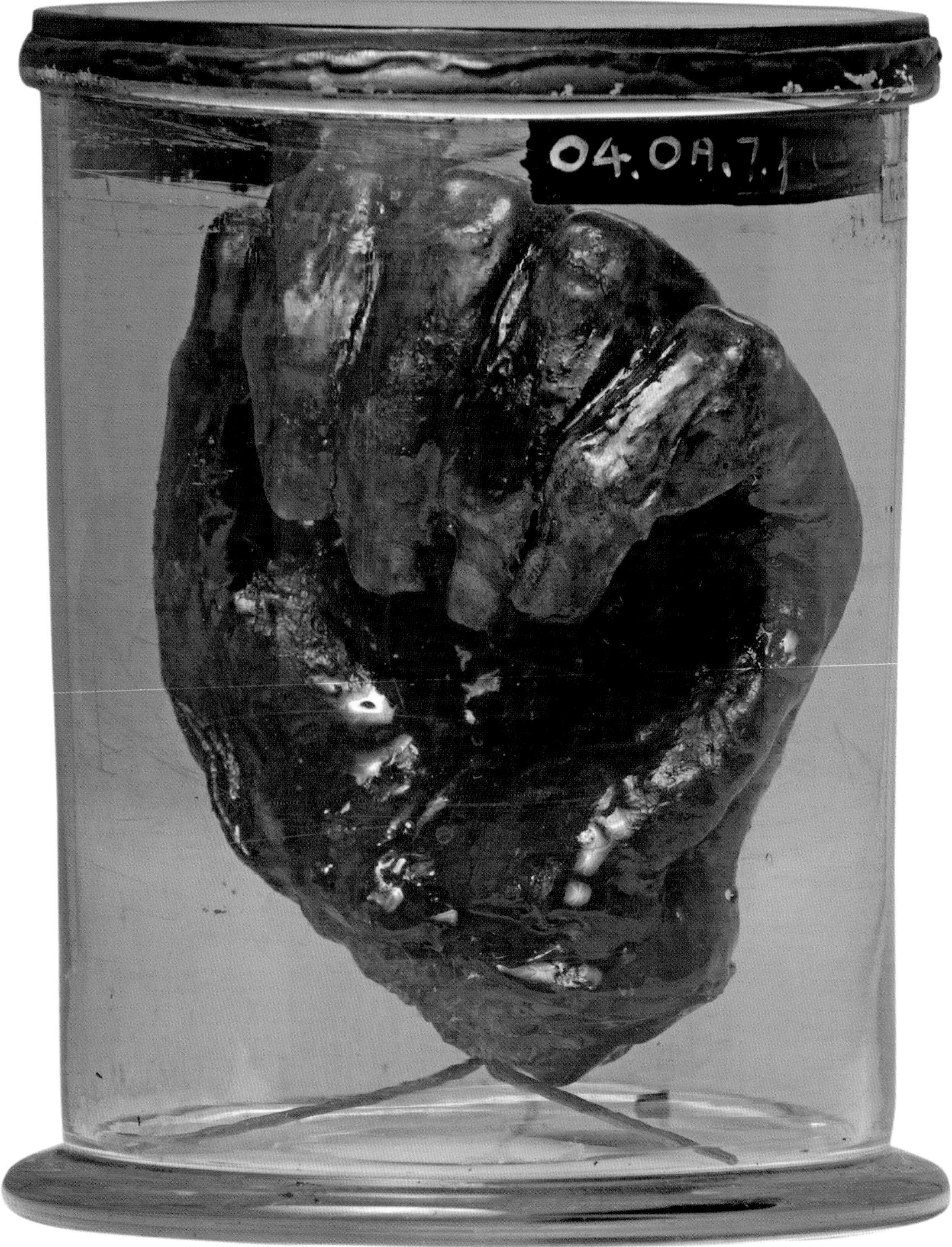
04.0A.7.

'Behold with what I point! The sketch followed of a hand outspread on a shield. – This hand, how exquisite in form and motion. But first turn over – use it and learn to admire!'

CHARLES BELL, letter to his brother, August 1830.

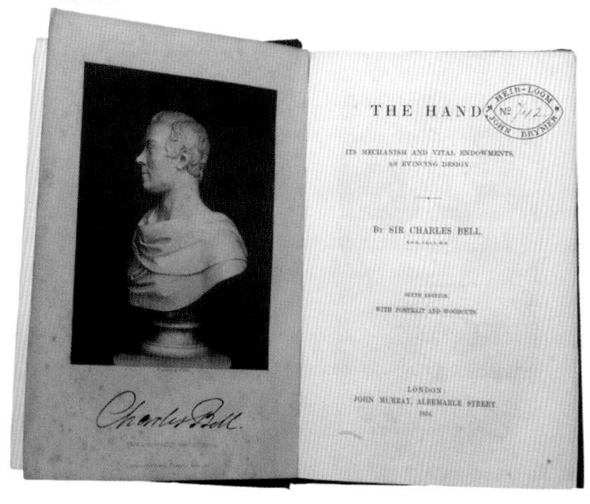

▲ **Hand** GC 11365.
Foot BC I.N.107 GC 12558.
Hand BC. I.N.98 GC 11354/6.

◀ **Adult left hand showing gangrene.**
B.C. iv.1.M.7. GC 11023.

▶ **Charles Bell's *The Hand, its Mechanism and Vital Endowments, as Evincing Design*.**
First published 1833. RCSEd Collections.

Surgeon Square 1790-1830s

John Bell (1763-1820), artist unknown.

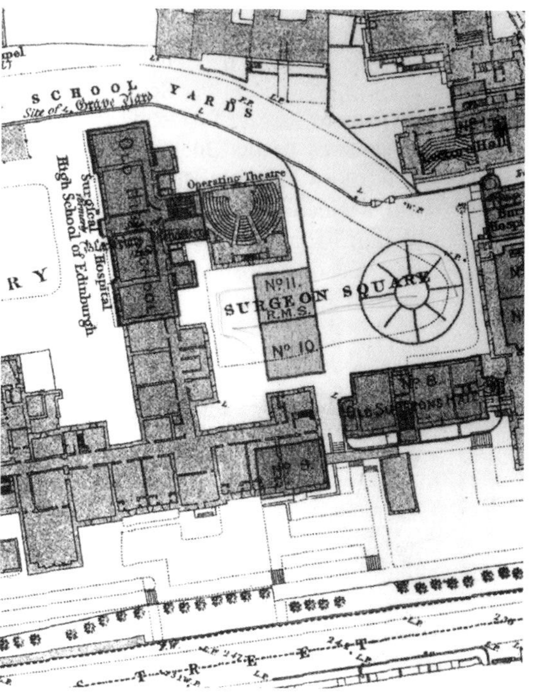

Detail from Ordnance Survey Map of Edinburgh, 1879.

JOHN BELL'S HOUSE

1790	John Bell opens anatomy school, the first to be licenced by the College of Surgeons.
1792	Charles Bell becomes apprenticed to John Bell and works alongside him at the anatomy school.
1799-1804	Charles Bell takes over formal teaching at John Bell's School.
1804	Charles Bell moves to London. House and school sold but continue to be used for anatomy lectures. Most of collection sent to Charles in London.
1826	RCSEd acquires house for new Bell and Barclay collections. Middle floor used to house specimens from John Barclay collection. Over 500 students visit the collection.
1833	House sold to the Managers of the Royal Infirmary of Edinburgh for £500.

SURGEONS' HALL, NO 8 SURGEON SQUARE

1787-1790	John Bell gives anatomy lectures in the Hall.
1804	New museum collection is established under Prof John Thomson.
1823	Two rooms at the west end of the Hall made into one and 'fitted with glass cases and shelving' to display some of the collection, bequested by John Barclay in 1821.
1825	RCSEd acquire house in Nicolson Street for some of Bell Collection.
1825/1826	Charles Bell's collection arrives in two consignments from London.
1831	Robert Knox resigns as conservator of RCSEd museums.
1833	Hall sold to the managers of the Royal Infirmary for £600. Robert Knox rents rooms in building for his anatomy lectures.

Hand painted watercolour of 10 and 11 Surgeon Square by Thomas Shepherd, 1829. The western corner of Surgeons' Hall is on the left.

NO 10 SURGEON SQUARE

1800-1826	John Barclay's school and museum. The lecture theatre was located on the top floor, with the dissecting room below it.
1804	Barclay's classes given formal recognition by the Royal College of Surgeons of Edinburgh for its Licentiate Diploma. Now teaching around 300 students per year.
1825	Robert Knox becomes Barclay's partner.
1826	John Barclay dies and ownership of his collection passes to the College of Surgeons under the conditions agreed in the deed of settlement of 1821.
1826-1833	Robert Knox uses building for anatomy teaching.

NO 11 SURGEON SQUARE

1776	Medical Society of Edinburgh first meeting held in new building.
1778	Medical Society awarded Royal Charter: Royal Medical Society of Edinburgh.
1825	RCSEd Council hold their meetings in the building.

Surgeon Square was the most important centre of medical education in Edinburgh during the early 19th century.

Robert Knox

The most famous of all Surgeons' Hall Museum conservators, Dr Robert Knox (1791-1862), was involved in almost every aspect of the museum's development during its great expansion of the 1820s and early 1830s.

In 1824 Robert Knox offered to make a new collection of comparative anatomy and physiology for the College of Surgeons, on the condition he could use it for his own teaching.

By the summer of 1825 he was well established as one of Edinburgh's most prominent anatomists. In January he had been appointed Conservator of the surgeons' anatomy collection; the following month, as their agent, he travelled to London with Alexander Watson, one of the keepers of the pathology museum, to inspect Charles Bell's collection. Soon after his return John Barclay, now aged 65 and keen to make arrangements for his retirement, offered Knox a partnership in his anatomy school and in April Knox qualified as a Fellow of the College of Surgeons.

Despite his new teaching commitments Knox continued to worked tirelessly in developing Surgeons' Hall's collections, arranging specimens and writing fulsome case notes in the General Catalogue. He personally directed the packing and transport of the Bell collection from London to Edinburgh, and produced a handwritten catalogue of the collection.

Caricature of Robert Knox, artist unknown.
RCSEd Collections.

'Posterity will have to be very clever, to judge you justly, Dr Knox.'

JAMES BRIDIE, *The Anatomist.*

Robert Knox's Diploma with wax seal from the Royal College of Surgeons of Edinburgh, 1825. RCSEd Collections.

Collegium Regium Chirurgorum Edinburgense

Decrevit ornatissimum virum Robertum Knox
examine solito feliciter peracto, in Societatem suam cooptare
et Collegam adsciscere. Ipsum ideo omnium honorum atque
privilegiorum quibus Socii ejusdem Collegii fruuntur participem
fecit. In cujus rei fidem hoc Diploma sigillo suo Præsidisque
chirographo munitum expediri jussit. Actum Edinburgi in
Conventu Chirurgorum die decimo nono mensis Aprilis
anno millesimo octingentesimo et vigesimo quinto

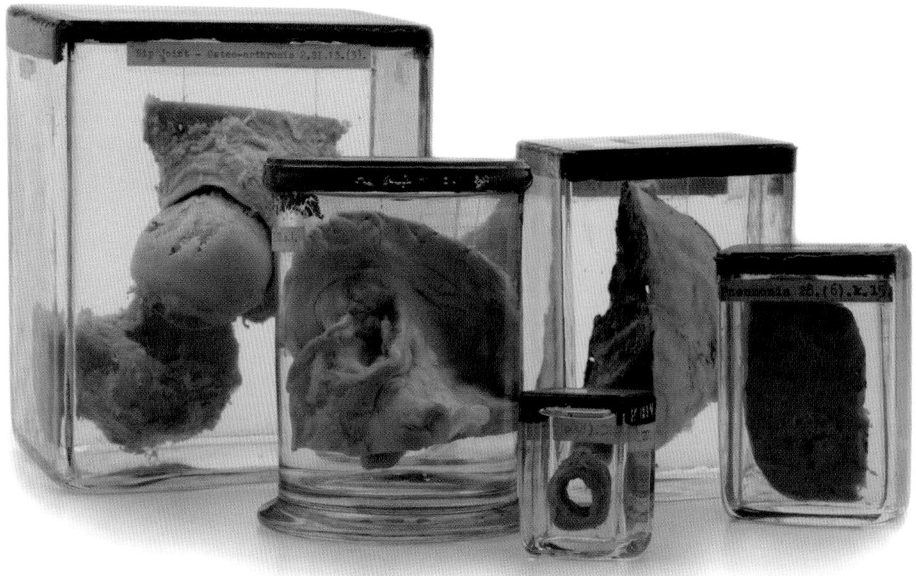

Specimens prepared by Robert Knox.
GC 1122, GC 1239, GC 1137, GC 1123.

In May 1826, for his efforts, but not without some opposition, Knox was finally elected to the new post of Museum Conservator of the Royal College of Surgeons of Edinburgh, with an annual salary of £150. John Barclay died in August the same year and his collection, as under the terms of its bequest became the property of the College, with Knox to be appointed Keeper and Conservator for life.

Knox's two Conservator roles of the Barclay Collection and the anatomy and pathology collections were merged in 1828. His influence on shaping the new museum was immense.

Knox was by now the most successful anatomist in Scotland, if not Britain. His brilliance in the subject and natural flamboyance in teaching attracted hundreds of students to his classes. One of them, Henry Lonsdale, later his partner and biographer, described him vividly:

'Knox, in the highest style of fashion, with spotless linen, frill, and lace, and jewellery redolent of a duchess's boudoir, standing in a class-room amid osseous forms, cadavers, and decaying mortalities, was a sight to behold, and one assuredly never to be forgotten...'

Knox was indeed a charismatic and dramatic figure, but it was his involvement in one of Britain's most infamous serial murder cases that led to him becoming the most fictionalised of all Scottish medical men.

Burke and Hare

The development of anatomy teaching in Edinburgh in the early nineteenth century led to an unprecedented demand for 'fresh' bodies for dissection by the anatomy schools.

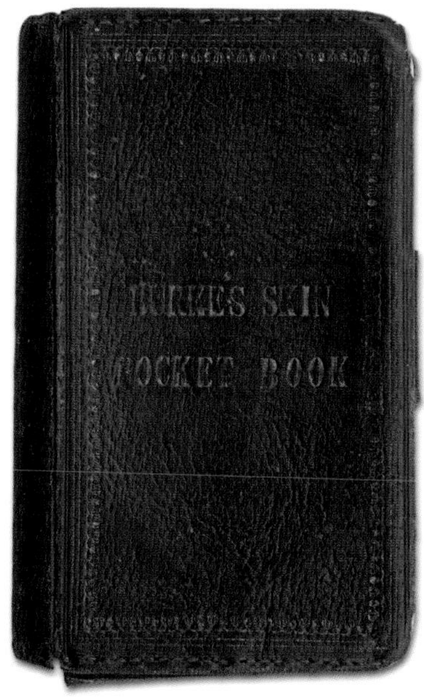

Pocketbook reputedly made from the skin of William Burke. RCSEd Collections.

Down the Close
and Up the Stairs
Ben the hoose with
Burke and Hare
Burkes the Butcher,
Hares the Thief
Knox the boy
who buys the beef.

Popular Edinburgh street rhyme dating from 1828/9.

The suppliers of the bodies, the 'grave-robbers' or 'resurrection men,' were the least regarded of all the participants in this golden era of medical education. However, an even more sinister source of supply was about to rock the medical establishment and hasten the introduction of Britain's first Anatomy Act in 1832.

In 1827, William Burke and William Hare by-passed the graveyards altogether and resorted to murder to supply bodies for anatomical dissection. By the time they were caught in November 1828 they had murdered at least 16 people and delivered their victims' bodies to Robert Knox's dissection room at Surgeon Square. Although Knox was never charged with any crime, debate surrounded his knowledge of how these human 'subjects' had met their deaths. Burke, after Hare gave testimony against him, was hung for murder in January 1829, and the judge ordered his body to be publicly dissected by the University Professor of Anatomy, Alexander Monro *tertius*.

There is no mention of the Burke and Hare murders in any of the College records and Knox continued as Museum Conservator. His medical peers were reluctant to make him a scapegoat lest their collective involvement in the Resurrectionists' trade came under greater scrutiny.

But his association with the scandal and what many thought an arrogance of character left him an easy target for professional rivals, some of them curators on the museum committee to which he reported. Within three years petty and largely unfounded complaints about his museum duties led to his resignation in July 1831, less than a year before the new Surgeons' Hall was to open.

Mr. K–

'There was, at that period, a certain extramural teacher of anatomy, whom I shall here designate by the letter K. His name was subsequently too well known.

The man who bore it skulked through the streets of Edinburgh in disguise, while the mob that applauded at the execution of Burke called loudly for the blood of his employer. But Mr K – was then at the top of his vogue; he enjoyed a popularity due partly to his own talent and address, partly to the incapacity of his rival, the university professor. The students at least swore by his name, and Fettes believed himself, and was believed by others to have laid the foundations of success when he had acquired the favour of this meteorically famous man. Mr K – was a bon vivant as well as an accomplished teacher...

...The supply of subjects was a continual problem to him [Fettes, Mr K's assistant] *as well as his master. In that large and busy class, the raw material of the anatomists kept perpetually running out, and the business thus rendered necessary was not only unpleasant in itself, but threatened dangerous consequences to all who were concerned. It was the policy of Mr K---- to ask no questions in his dealings with the trade. "They bring the boy, and we pay the price" he used to say, dwelling on the alliteration – quid pro quo. And again, and somewhat profanely, "Ask no questions" he would tell his assistants, "for conscience sake".'*

ROBERT LOUIS STEVENSON, *The Bodysnatcher,* 1881.

Photograph of Robert Knox, taken at Rock House Studios Calton Hill, Edinburgh from an original calotype negative by David Octavius Hill c 1843. RCSEd Collections.

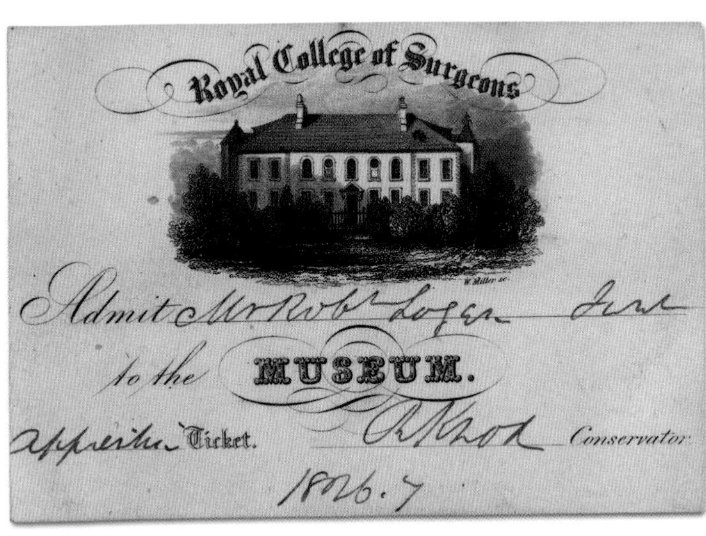

Class Card for the Museum of the Royal College of Surgeons of Edinburgh for the session 1826/27. It is signed by Robert Knox and shows Surgeons' Hall. RCSEd Collections.

The Anatomist

The Anatomist, a play about Robert Knox, was written by James Bridie and first performed in 1930. It met with wide critical acclaim and commercial success in London and Scotland.

'***Knox:*** *The comparative anatomist has curiosity. He institutes a divine search for facts. He is unconcerned with explanations and theories. In time when you and I are dead, His facts will be collected and their sum will be the Truth. Truth that will show the noblest thing in creation, how to live. Truth that will shatter the idol Mumbo Jumbo, before which man daily debases his magnificence. Truth…*

Mary: *Do you call the hands of the resurrectionist clean?*

Knox: *Of the blood of the innocent*

Mary: *Grave Robbing is worse than murder*

Knox: *Madam you are a pagan atheist to say so. If you believed in an immortal soul, why should you venerate the empty shell it has spurned in its upward flight? And with a false veneration too. The anatomist alone has a reverence for the human body, He loves it. He knows it.*

Mary: *He pays ruffians to tear it from the grave where loving hands have laid it. Your friend Mr Liston, the surgeon, goes himself and beats the guardians like the pit-house bully he is.*

Knox: *Bob Liston is no friend of mine…I abhor his methods.*

Mary: *Where do you get your bodies from?*

Knox: *How should I know? My duty is to teach.*'

NEW PLAY.—Henry Ainley (left), Carlton Hobbs, and Betty Hardy in "The Anatomist," the new play which was produced last night at the Westminster Theatre.

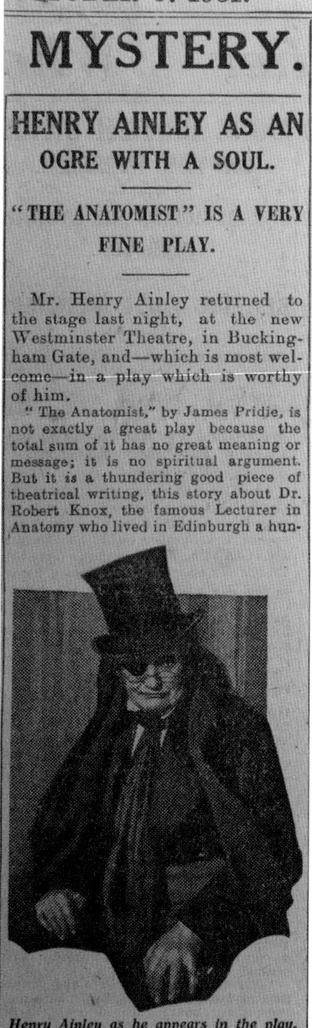

OCTOBER 8. 1931.

MYSTERY.

HENRY AINLEY AS AN OGRE WITH A SOUL.

"THE ANATOMIST" IS A VERY FINE PLAY.

Mr. Henry Ainley returned to the stage last night, at the new Westminster Theatre, in Buckingham Gate, and—which is most welcome—in a play which is worthy of him.

"The Anatomist," by James Pridie, is not exactly a great play because the total sum of it has no great meaning or message; it is no spiritual argument. But it is a thundering good piece of theatrical writing, this story about Dr. Robert Knox, the famous Lecturer in Anatomy who lived in Edinburgh a hun-

Henry Ainley as he appears in the play.

▲ Newspaper reviews of *The Anatomist*
▶ performed at the Westminster Theatre, 1931.
RCSEd Collections.

For 180 years Knox has endured as an enigmatic but often sinister figure in popular culture: from street rhymes and books to plays and films. The dramatic fascination with Knox's character shows no sign of waning. Most recently Ian Rankin's *The Falls* (2001), Nicola Morgan's *Fleshmarket* (2003), a screenplay *The Meat Trade* penned by Irvine Welsh and a new film directed by John Landis, look set to propel Knox well into his third century.

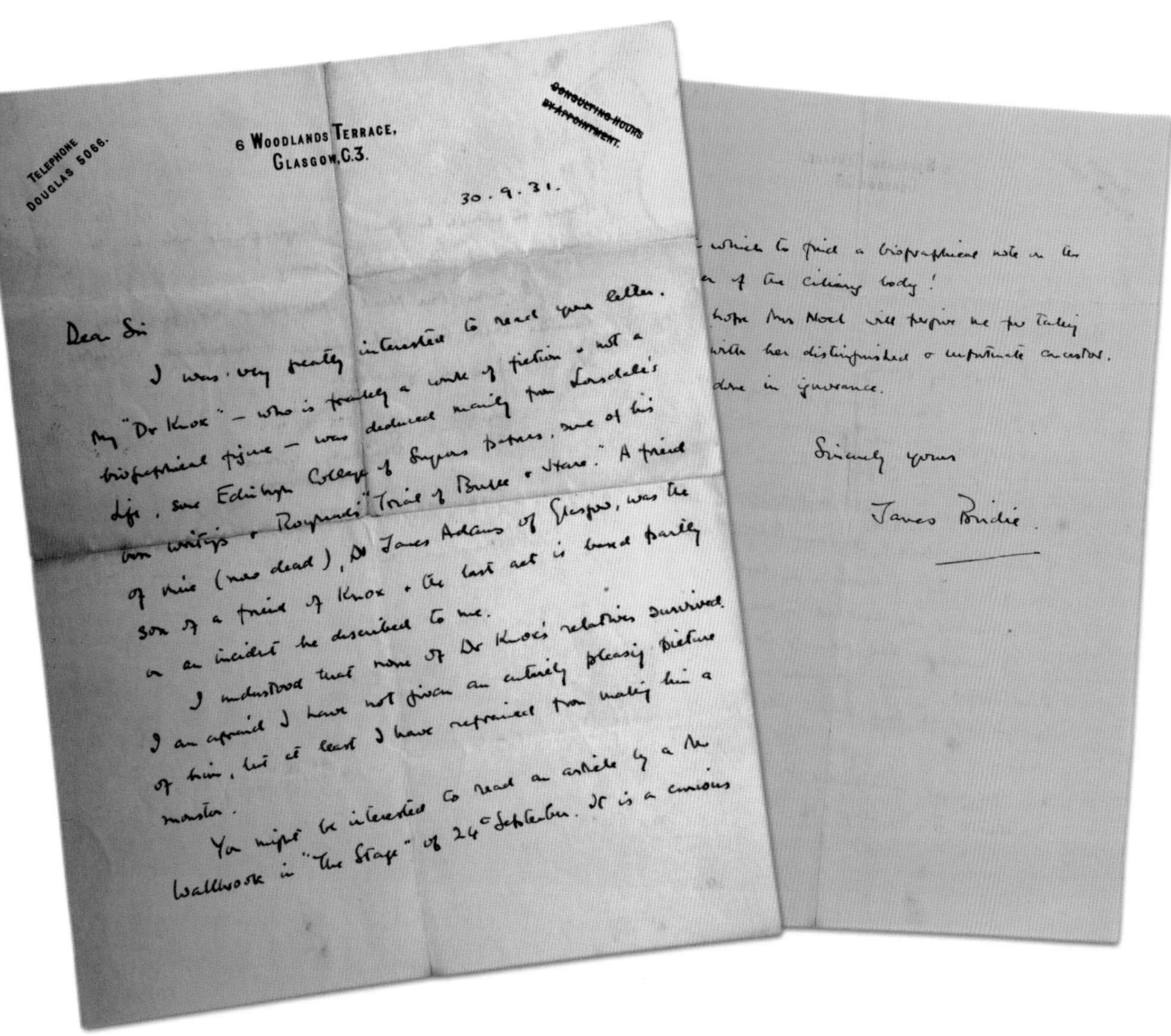

TELEPHONE DOUGLAS 5066.

6 WOODLANDS TERRACE,
GLASGOW, C.3.

CONSULTING HOURS BY APPOINTMENT.

30.9.31.

Dear Sir

I was very greatly interested to read your letter. My "Dr Knox" – who is frankly a work of fiction & not a biographical figure – was deduced mainly from Lonsdale's Life, some Edinburgh College of Surgeons papers, some of his own writings & Roughead's "Trial of Burke & Hare." A friend of mine (now dead), Dr James Adams of Glasgow, was the son of a friend of Knox & the last act is based partly on an incident he described to me.

I understood that none of Dr Knox's relatives survived. I am afraid I have not given an entirely pleasing picture of him, but at least I have refrained from making him a monster.

You might be interested to read an article by a Mr Wallbrook in "The Stage" of 24th September. It is a curious [illegible] which to find a biographical note on the [illegible] of the [illegible] body!

[illegible] hope Mrs Noel will forgive me for taking [illegible] with her distinguished & unfortunate ancestor. [illegible] done in ignorance.

Sincerely yours

James Bridie

Letter from James Bridie to Robert Knox's grandson. *'I am afraid I have not given an entirely pleasing picture of him, but at least I have refrained from making him a monster,'* 1931. RCSEd Collections.

SURGEONS. EDINBURGH. 384.

New Surgeons' Hall

The problem of accommodation for the new collections became a pressing one. An option to build a new hall on the old Surgeon Square site was finally closed in 1828 and various new sites were considered. The Royal Riding School situated slightly south of, but on higher ground than, the University College was chosen. William Playfair was appointed architect and work started in 1829. The new Surgeons' Hall was officially opened on 7th July 1832.

▲ **John Gairdner,** President of the Royal College of Surgeons of Edinburgh 1832, RCSEd Collections.

◀ **Surgeons' Hall,** Edinburgh c1880. © RCAHMS.

The opening ceremony was reported in *The Scotsman* on the 14 July 1832,

> '*...we have the best authority to add that it has been erected solely at the expence* (sic) *of the College, without the aid of those Parliamentary Grants which have been freely given to similar institutions elsewhere.*
>
> *They (the guests) proceeded to examine the different museums which are upon the floor above. The first apartment on that floor is appropriated exclusively to the splendid collection bequeathed to the College by the late Dr Barclay, consisting of specimens of anatomy, human and comparative, and of natural history. The next...contains the Museum partly acquired by purchase from Sir C Bell (Charles) and partly accumulated by the exertions of the Royal College during the last twenty five years. Dr Gardiner* (sic)*, presented to the company a general invitation to visit the Museums of the College as frequently as possible, and explained the nature of the regulations regarding the admission of visitors, which are so liberal, that every class of person, unprofessional as well as professional, may have access to these collections without any restrictions but such as are plainly requisite for their safe custody.*'

William Playfair

William Henry Playfair (1789-1857), the architect of the new Surgeons' Hall, was born in London. In 1794 after his father's death he was sent to live in Edinburgh with his uncle, Professor John Playfair, a leading figure of the Scottish Enlightenment.

He is celebrated as the architect of many of Edinburgh's most significant public buildings and landmarks including the Royal Scottish Academy, the National Gallery of Scotland, the National Monument, the General Assembly Hall, the Advocates Library, and the Library of Edinburgh University. Playfair drew on many different styles for his buildings from Gothic and Tudor to Italianate, but it was his expertise in the Greek Revival form of Classical architecture which sealed his fame and earned Edinburgh the title 'Athens of the North.'

William Playfair, the architect of Surgeons' Hall.

The floor plan of the Pathology Museum on the first floor of Surgeons' Hall, designed especially to house the Bell collection and the early pathology specimens collected by the College since 1804. Photo Max McKenzie.

Surgeons' Hall, Edinburgh by William Henry Playfair RSA, pencil and wash, c.1829-1832. Playfair became a member of the Royal Scottish Academy (RSA) in 1829 and presented this drawing of Surgeons' Hall in 1836 as his 'diploma' work. By permission: Royal Scottish Academy (Diploma Collection).

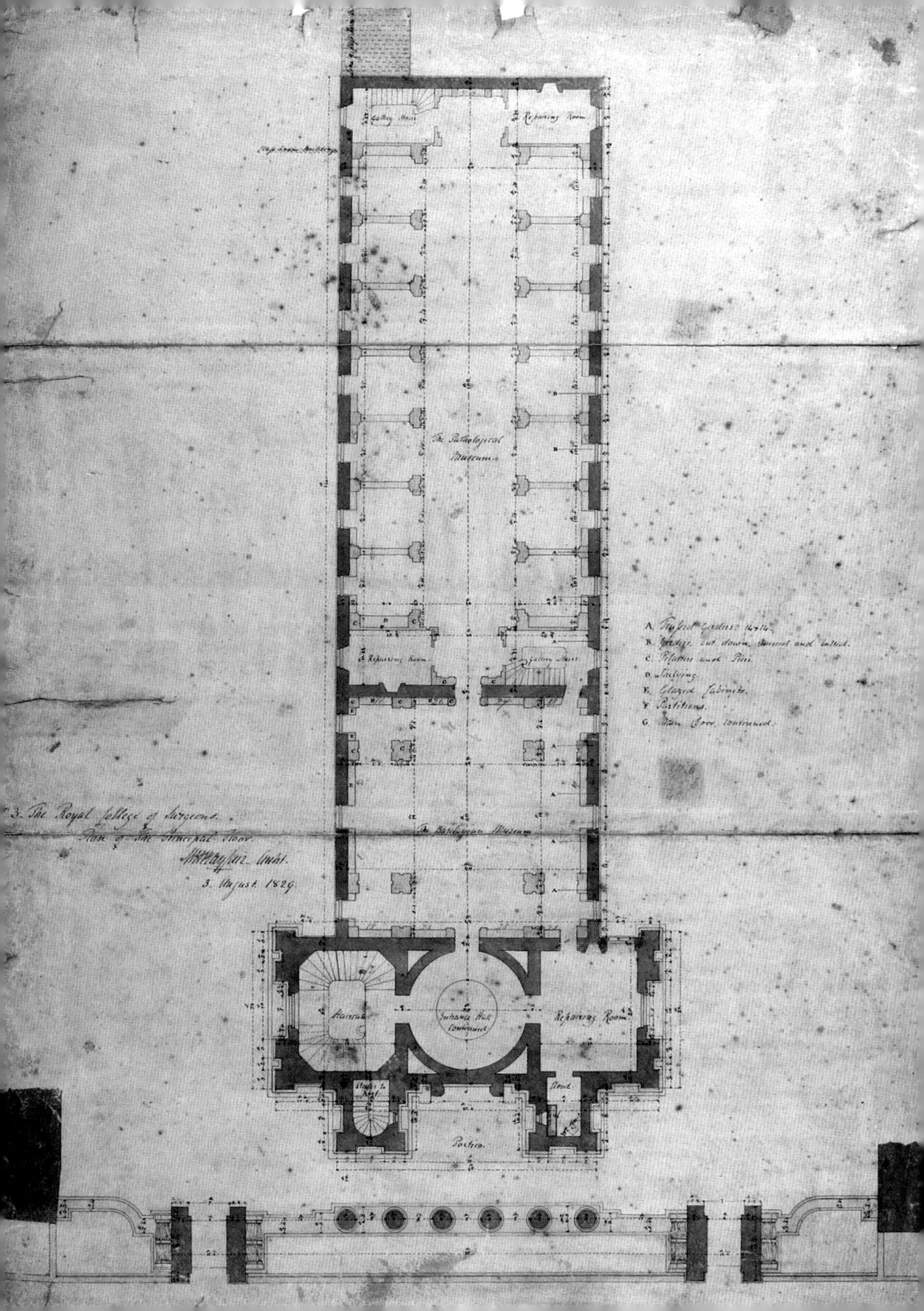

The Pathological Museum
Repairing Room
Repairing Room
Gallery Stairs
Gallery Stairs
Repairing Room
C. Pilasters and Piers.
D. Shelving.
E. Glazed Cabinets.
F. Partitions.
G. Main Floor continued.
3. The Royal College of Surgeons.
3. August 1829
Staircase
Entrance Hall continued
Repairing Room
Portico

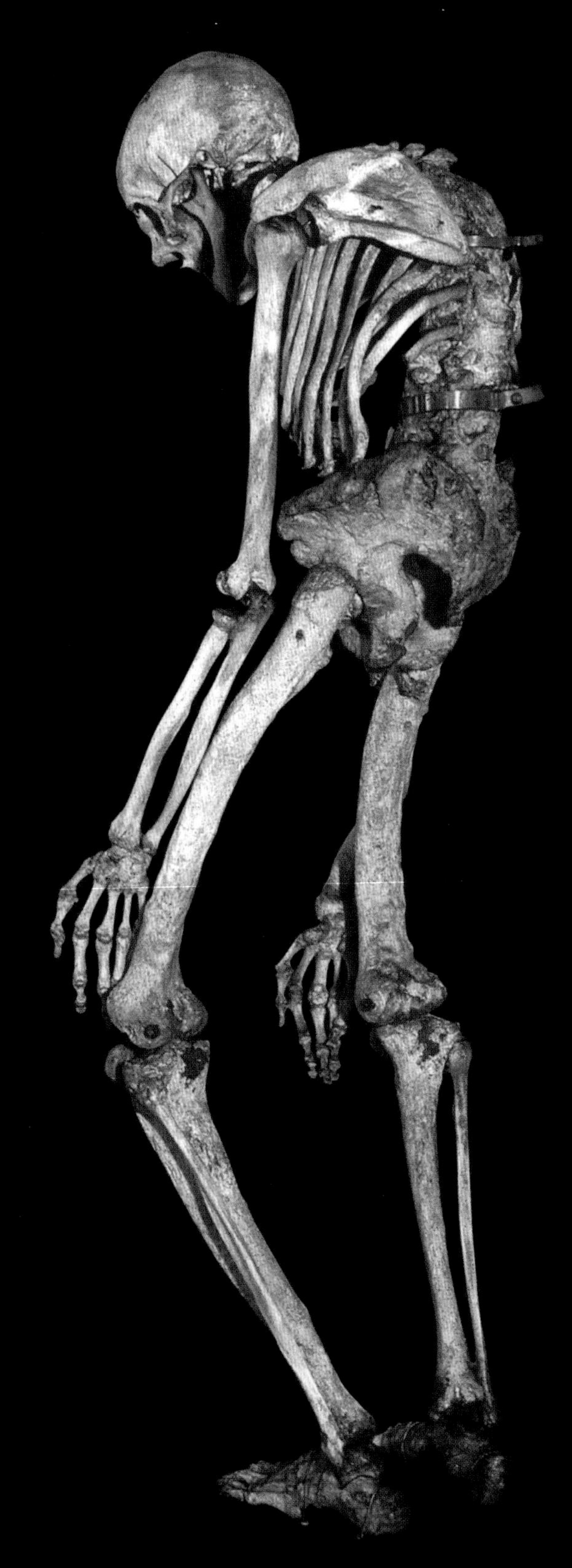

Corpus Vile

CHRISTINE DE LUCA

Some museums of antiquities store row on row of
unnamed skulls. There is a day of reckoning now
a plea to repatriate lost souls, bring home bones

to territorial rest. Is it surprising the rituals we wrap
round death? Anguish felt at bodies missing, ungraved,
when loss is certain? How many symbolic coffins

have been lowered, wounds eased with the thud
of gentle earth on unimagined emptiness? There is
fierce beauty in a skeleton picked clean as carrion,

a recycling of our elementalness. Here, in this museum,
skeletons catalogued and studied carefully are unlikely
to raise a court case. Few would want these bones back,

a rickle of deformity. Yet there is grace in these harp
shapes: curved, sculptural. A spine bent back upon itself,
with vertebrae on which a seraph might make music.

I remember visiting a little girl in hospital, one Sunday,
a steel rod newly planted in her clarsach of a back. By the
next Sunday, stringed melody: for her, *hinc sanitas*.

Leaving the museum, how fine to see children jostle
for a bus; tall, straight; even their teeth wondrously
aligned, their body temples still unplundered.

Skeleton showing Pagets disease, a chronic bone disorder of the spine. GC 13522.

William MacGillivray

The transfer of the collections to the new Surgeons' Hall was completed by William MacGillivray (1796-1852), who succeeded Knox as Museum conservator in August 1831.

'He had singular qualifications as Keeper of a Museum. Nothing could exceed his care and patience in preparing an object, except perhaps the delight with which he contemplated the result. His taste in displaying, and his neatness in arranging, were alike remarkable; and both the valuable Museums so long under his care were much indebted to his assiduous labours.'

A.THOMPSON, *Edinburgh New Philosophical Journal* (1853).

William MacGillivray, Museum Curator, 1831-41. This work may be a copy of a watercolour completed in oil by his daughter Anne.

'Dr Barclay's Collection is contained in a beautiful and well lighted apartment forty feet square, furnished with glazed cases and a gallery. It consists of 2512 preparations, arranged in three series, under the heads of Human Anatomy and Pathology, Comparative Anatomy, Fossils and Miscellanea.

In the department of Human Anatomy, there are 770 articles: viz, in spirits 60, in turpentine 10, dry 689, casts 3, engravings 8...

In the department of Comparative Anatomy, there are 1457 preparations: viz., in spirits 234, in turpentine 5, dry 799, shells 245, eggs 174. Among these are many valuable skeletons of mammals, including those of the Asiatic Elephant, Dromedary, Walrus, and Narwhal, together with an extensive series of skulls, and numerous specimens of teeth...

...Considered as the collection of a private individual formed at his own expense, with no other aid than that occasionally afforded by his pupils, it is a monument of zeal and energy; although as a public museum it does not contain enough of specimens to illustrate the various organs of animals in the extended series disclosed by modern Zoology. Taken in connection with the preparations made by the late and present Conservators of the Museum of the Royal College of Surgeons, it affords an important aid to the student of this delightful branch of science.'

WILLIAM MACGILLIVRAY *Naturalists Library* XI 1841.

MacGillivray, although not medically qualified, had considerable museum experience. As assistant to Professor Robert Jameson, he had supervised Edinburgh University's renowned Natural History Museum since 1822.

MacGillivray's greatest interest was in natural history and especially birds. During his time at Surgeons' Hall he worked closely with the celebrated ornithologist John James Audubon (1785-1851) who lived in Edinburgh intermittently for almost three years between 1826 and 1839.

Eagle Owl (Bubo Bubo) drawing by William MacGillivray in *A History of British Birds*, 1837-52. Audubon presented this eagle owl to MacGillivray when it was still alive. It lived in Surgeons' Hall Museum until its death. Its skin was kept and is now in the collections of the National Museums of Scotland; it was exhibited at Surgeons Hall in 2003 as part of the exhibition *Audubon in Edinburgh*.

John James Audubon painted in Edinburgh by John Syme, 1826. White House Historical Association (White House Collection).

MacGillivray provided the scientific information for Audubon's *Ornithological Biography*, the text which accompanied his brilliant life size paintings, engraved and published as *The Birds of America*. MacGillivray also taught Audubon how to dissect birds while Audubon encouraged MacGillivray's talent as a wildlife artist.

As conservator MacGillivray was subject to stricter conditions of employment than Robert Knox. He was forbidden from keeping a personal museum and could only give lectures or leave the city with permission from the museum committee. His daily duties included cataloguing, labelling, preserving, cleaning, arranging and dissecting specimens and supervising visits. The new Surgeons' Hall museums were open four days a week, Tuesday to Friday, noon-4pm in summer, 3pm in winter, and true to Gairdner's address in 1832 they were open to 'every class of person.'

Hard Times

The expense of building and operating the new Surgeons' Hall was not without financial strain on the College. In 1837 an application, in the form of a 'memorial' was made by the President and Fellows of the Royal College of Surgeons of Edinburgh to 'His Majesty's Treasury' for a grant. The memorial presented their case:

'…The Museum is gratuitously open to the inspection of all classes of the public (the number of visitors being about 10,000), the effect of which, there is every reason to believe, has been to diminish the prejudices against post mortem examinations, as well as to facilitate the beneficial operation of the Anatomy Bill, and thus both to advance the progress of science and promote the well-being of society.

…That the whole funds of the Corporation, with the exception of what has been spent in the ordinary business of the College, conducted on a scale of rigid economy, have been devoted to the collection, purchase and preservation of the preparations in their Museum, and to the erection of a building principally for their proper reception and useful arrangements, on which objects the Memorialists have expended the sum of £.27,000.

…In the attainment of what may truly be considered a national object – the establishment of an extensive Anatomical and Pathological Museum, at the seat of a great Medical School, freely and gratuitously opened to the Medical Profession and to the Public, – have not only entirely exhausted their funds, but have incurred a debt upwards of £.8,000. This, the Memorialists have reason to fear, must greatly embarrass their efforts to maintain their Museum in a state of efficiency and to extend its usefulness…'

Parliamentary Papers, 1838. Application by the RCSEd to Government for grant towards defraying debts from the building of new Surgeons Hall and the cost of the museum collections.

The Treasury agreed to the application for a grant and awarded the College £5,000. In November 1837 the College received a letter from the Lord Advocate, John Murray, asking how the grant had been used and *'what regulations have been adopted at the Museum of the College of Surgeons for the admission of the public, and whether any inconvenience of any sort has been experienced from admitting the public, or any additional precautions required or expense incurred on that account.'*

George Ballingall (1780-1855), President of the Royal College of Surgeons of Edinburgh 1836-38.

George Balingall, President of the College replied:

'*... I have the honor* (sic) *to state that the Museum of the Royal College of Surgeons, ever since it was placed in the new Hall and in a fit state for exhibition, has been open to the public without any further restriction... There is reason to believe that the privilege of admission to the Museum is highly valued by the public at large and that something has been done in this quarter towards reconciling the minds of the lower orders to the necessity and advantages of Anatomical and Pathological investigations.*'

A report from William MacGillivray was also included in which he added:

'*... Visitors of the lower classes, mechanics, sailors and soldiers have uniformly been quiet, careful and most orderly... visitors of the lower classes seem to take more interest in the specimens than those of the higher, many of whom, especially ladies, merely walk through the rooms without looking at the objects particularly.*'

The conditions of the government grant obliged the College to keep its collections open to the public. But with annual fees from fewer than one hundred members the expense of running such a large building and looking after extensive collections still placed a large financial burden on the College. The need to cut costs was to lead to a reduction in museum activities in the 1840s.

1840s and 50s

William MacGillivray resigned in 1841 on being appointed Professor of Civil and Natural History at Marischal College, Aberdeen University. From 1841 to 1845 the post of conservator was held successively by John Goodsir and his younger brothers Harry and, briefly, Archibald.

The only notable improvement to the collections during this period was the introduction, by John Goodsir, of painted catalogue numbers on jars, designed to overcome the problem of labels falling off and specimens becoming unidentifiable.

College economies led to a reduction in the conservator's pay to £100 pa and in 1847 the Goodsirs' successor Hamlin Lee was given the additional responsibilities of College Librarian and Officer to the College. For a while in the late1840s, to save cleaning costs, the Pathology Museum was also closed to the public.

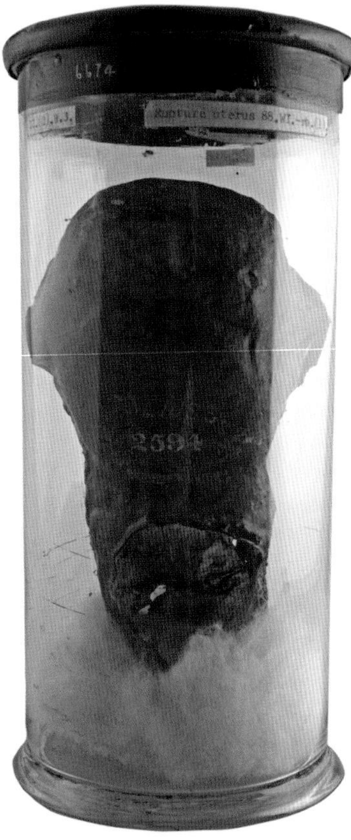

▲ **Specimen showing the new system, introduced by John Goodsir, of marking the museum specimens.** Black numbers for those in the general catalogue and white for those included in MacGillivray's first printed catalogue. GC 6674.

◀ **John Goodsir,** Museum Conervator 1841-3.

Iris of the eye of the ox, 1850. This is the earliest glass slide identified in Surgeons' Hall's collections. It is thought to have been prepared by Hamlin Lee, conservator from 1845-53. RSCEd Collections.

Compound Monocular Microscope, c. 1840. On loan from the National Museums of Scotland.

By the1850s, despite continuing financial pressures on the College, external factors were to play their part in moving the museum into new areas of activity.

The 1840s had seen the establishment of the use of the microscope in medicine. John Goodsir's *Anatomical and Pathological Observations* published in 1845 promoted its use in the study of tissue at a minute level, what is now called, histology. In the following year the museum curators 'rendered necessary by the direction which anatomical and physiological investigations have recently taken' supported Hamlin Lee's work in forming a series of microscopic preparations on glass slides. This was the beginning of the museum's histology collection.

Apart from the University, extra mural schools were a significant aspect of the teaching offered to medical students in Edinburgh throughout the nineteenth century. By the 1850s many classes were based at Surgeons' Hall, in fact in a building slightly to the north east of the Playfair building. Although it also contained a private museum collection owned by the lecturers, the students at the school were also tutored by Fellows of the college and museum conservators and curators in the main Surgeons' Hall Museum.

▲ Medical School at Surgeons' Hall c. 1890.

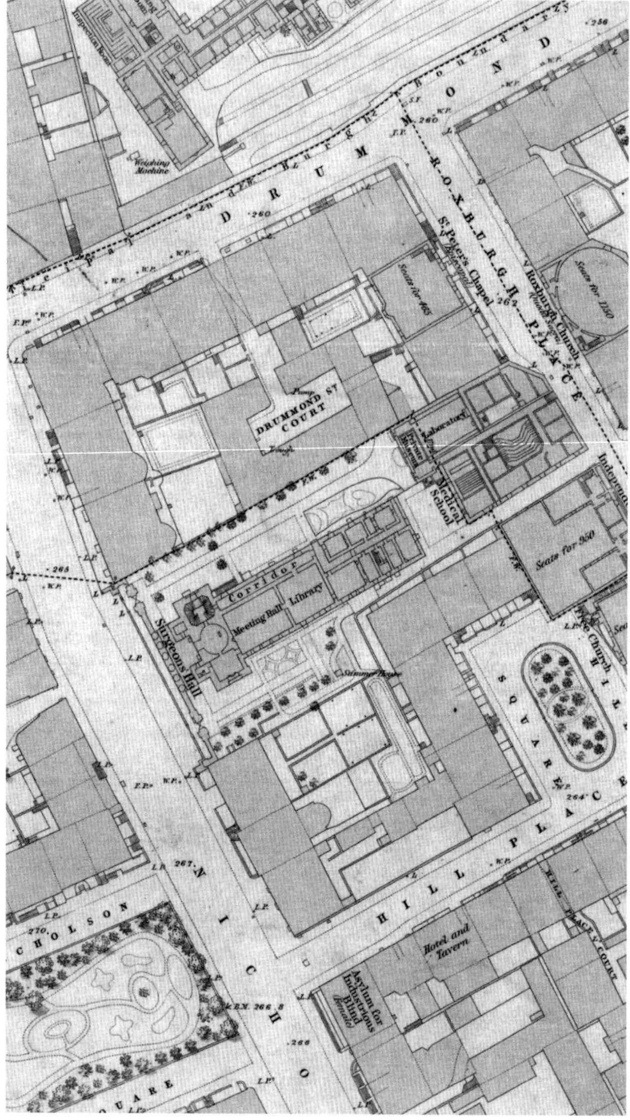

◀ **Detail from the Ordnance Survey Map of Edinburgh 1853** showing the ground floor of the main Playfair building and Surgeons' Hall 'Medical School'. National Library of Scotland.

▶ **Extract from 1856/7 Parliamentary Report on Medical Museums.**

271

MEDICAL MUSEUMS.

RETURN to an Address of the Honourable The House of Commons, dated 17 July 1856;—*for*,

"RETURNS from the COLLEGES of PHYSICIANS of *London*, *Edinburgh*, and *Ireland*, the COLLEGES of SURGEONS of *England*, *Edinburgh*, and *Ireland*, the FACULTY of PHYSICIANS and SURGEONS of *Glasgow*, the SOCIETIES of APOTHECARIES of *London* and *Dublin*, and the UNIVERSITIES in *England*, *Scotland* and *Ireland*, stating, whether any MUSEUM for MEDICAL PURPOSES is maintained out of the Funds of the Institution; under what Conditions such Museum, if any, is open to Students or Members of the Medical Profession; the Annual Cost of such Museum in each of the last Ten Years, distinguishing the Expenditure for Building, for Salaries and Wages, for Catalogues, and for Preserving and Increasing the Collection; the Total Number of the Catalogued Specimens in each of the last Ten Years; what Lectureships for Medical Purposes are maintained by the Funds of the Institution, and at what Annual Cost; under what Conditions have the Lectures, if any, been Open to the Public, or to Students, or Members of the Medical Profession; whether any Expenses have been incurred for Medical Libraries, Botanic Gardens, or other Objects of Medical Science, and, if so, at what average Annual Cost for the last Ten Years, and under what Conditions available to the Public or to Students or Members of the Medical Profession."

ROYAL COLLEGE OF SURGEONS, EDINBURGH.

Royal College of Surgeons, Edinburgh.

1. THE Royal College of Surgeons, of Edinburgh, have for many years possessed an extensive and valuable museum for medical purposes, to the maintenance of which the whole of their surplus income is devoted.

2. The museum is open every lawful day, except Tuesday, from 11 a.m. till 3 p.m. in winter, and from 11 a.m. till 4 p.m. in summer. Fellows and licentiates of the college have free access to the museum; the registered students of the Royal College are admitted on presenting their registration ticket. Professors of the University, fellows of the Royal Society, and of the Royal College of Physicians, and medical officers of the army and navy, have access at all times by tickets, which the conservator of the museum is authorised to issue. The public generally are admitted by the order of a fellow or a licentiate, or by application to the conservator at the museum, which is never refused in the case of any respectable applicant.

The museum is open at extra hours to fellows giving lectures, and their pupils. In short, the museum is practically as much open to the medical profession and the public as is possible, consistently with due regard to its preservation.

3. The museum of the College occupies the entire upper and larger portion of their hall buildings, which were erected in 1831-32, chiefly for its accommodation and proper display. There has consequently been no expenditure for buildings during

Royal College of Surgeons, Edinburgh.

during the last ten years, though considerable sums have been expended in repairs of the buildings; but, in lieu thereof, it has been thought proper to include in the following table an annual sum in name of rent, calculated at a moderate percentage upon the estimated outlay upon that portion of the buildings occupied by the museum, along also with a proportional part of the feu-duty (ground-rent), insurance and taxes:

YEARS.	Rent, Feu Duty, Insurance, and Taxes.			Salaries and Wages.			Miscellaneous Expenses.			TOTAL.		
	£.	s.	d.	£.	s.	d.	£.	s.	d.	£.	s.	d.
1846-47 - - - -	574	3	7½	140	10	–	23	8	5	738	2	–½
1847-48 - - - -	573	12	–½	147	16	–	20	11	7	742	9	7½
1848-49 - - - -	573	11	–	141	–	–	27	2	9	741	13	9
1849-50 - - - -	576	–	1	147	19	6	8	2	2	722	1	9
1850-51 - - - -	569	19	3	141	–	–	23	10	–½	734	9	3½
1851-52 - - - -	573	15	4½	140	6	–	13	5	11	736	7	3½
1852-53 - - - -	548	8	–	159	5	9	27	5	7	734	19	4
1853-54 - - - -	541	7	9	139	5	–	27	13	11½	708	6	10½
1854-55 - - - -	567	4	–	129	7	–	22	2	6	718	13	6
1855-56 - - - -	566	3	6¾	139	12	8½	182	1	5½	887	17	8¾

4. The museum of the Royal College contains the following numbers of catalogued specimens, viz.:

1. Healthy human anatomy - - - -	1,260
2. Midwifery - - - - - - - -	370
3. Morbid human anatomy - - - -	3,251
4. Comparative anatomy - - - - - -	1,475
TOTAL number of catalogued specimens - - -	6,356

There is, in addition, a large number of specimens not catalogued.

Within the last ten years the chief labour and expense have been bestowed on the repairs, preservation, and arrangement of the large collection already accumulated; the number of specimens added to the museum during that time has in consequence been very small. In 1854 fifty specimens were added, and about the same number were added in 1851, and also in 1847.

5. In the year 1804, when there existed no chair of surgery in the University of Edinburgh, the College established a professorship of surgery, which was held in succession by the late Dr. John Thomson, Dr. John W. Turner, and by Mr. J. Lizars, with the title of Professor of Surgery to the Royal College of Surgeons of Edinburgh, and for whom a lecture-room and other appliances of his class was provided by the College. Upon the establishment of the chair of surgery in the University, in the year 1832, the necessity of the College professorship no longer existed, and it was then discontinued.

The following lectures have been given, free of charge, to the members and students of the College within the last three years in the museum. Lectures and demonstrations on the specimens of morbid anatomy in 1854 and 1855, by Dr. Sanders, F.R.C.P., conservator of the museum. Lectures and demonstrations of comparative anatomy of the vertebrata, by Dr. John Struther, F.R.C.S.E. Lectures and demonstrations on the surgical preparations, by Mr. Spence and Mr. Lister, lecturers on surgery, to their pupils.

Lectures are also given, under the sanction of the College and in its hall, in the winter and spring seasons, by fellows of the College and others. On these latter occasions, as many gentlemen are invited as the hall can contain. The subjects being various, the invitations are issued to various classes of persons, according to their nature. Last winter there were four lectures, and the parties invited were, the Lord Provost and magistrates, and the Town Council, Fellows of the Royal Society and Royal College of Physicians, judges of the supreme courts, and other

Royal College of Surgeons, Edinburgh.

other lawyers; clergymen of all denominations, professors in the University, practitioners of medicine in Edinburgh, and in the country; scientific characters and many private citizens. In all, there were about 1,000 invitations issued to the four lectures.

There was no expense on these occasions except that of providing tea and coffee for the guests of the College, and this, of course, was trifling in amount.

The contents of the museum of the College were largely made available for illustrating the lectures, which excited much interest, and were resorted to from great distances.

6. In the year 1763 the College entered into an arrangement with the University, whereby they handed over to the University library a valuable and extensive collection of medical and other works, and at the same time became bound to pay an annual contribution of 5 *l.* in consideration of their obtaining for their fellows the perpetual privilege of borrowing books, &c. from the library of the University. For upwards of 30 years the college, in point of fact, voluntarily paid an additional annual contribution of 15 *l.* to the University library (besides occasional donations), and discontinued the increased annual payments, in consequence of the diminished state of their income, and large amount of debt, which they had been obliged to incur in building and fitting up their new hall and museum room. Now that this state of matters has to a great extent altered for the better, the college have the expectation of being enabled shortly to renew their former larger annual contribution.

The College has of late years formed the nucleus of a private library, but it is still inconsiderable, for want of adequate funds. It is accessible to all fellows of the College, and there is a reading room connected with it, supplied with medical and other periodical publications. The aggregate payments for the last 10 years to this collection of works have amounted to 194 *l.* 9 *s.*

The College have never incurred any expenses on account of botanic gardens, or subjects of medical science, except of the nature stated in this return.

Medical Licenses.

Note.—In the print of the return made by this College, in obedience to Order of the House of Commons, relating to "Medical Licenses," an inadvertent mistake has been made, where, after stating (under the first head, p. 54), that the number of fellows admitted during the last 10 years was 27, it is also made to appear that that was also the total number of fellows of the College then existing, whereas, in point of fact, the total number of fellows at the date of the return (29 April 1856) was 96.

In name and by authority of the College,

Andrew Wood, M.D.,
President.

New Additions

In the second half of the nineteenth century the museum began to grow again and emerging surgical specialisms became well represented through valuable private collections donated by Fellows of the College.

The museum profile was also enhanced by the involvement, as curators, of many famed surgical operators and pioneers. The only known Museum Committee Minute Book to survive dates from 1859-80 and includes in the lists of curators: James Syme (1799-1870); Peter Handyside (1808-81); James Spence (1812-82); James Miller (1812-64); William Walker (1814-85); Francis Imlach (1819-91); Joseph Lister (1827-1912); Patrick Heron Watson (1832-1907); William Turner (1832-1916); Joseph Bell (1837-1911); Douglas Argyll Robertson (1837-1909); Thomas Annandale (1838-1907); John Chiene (1843-1823) and John Halliday Croom (1847-1923).

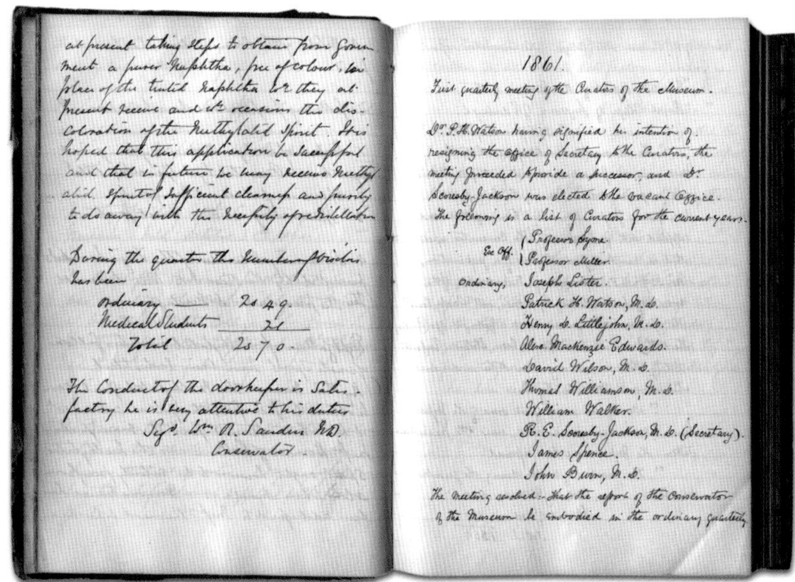

at present taking steps to obtain from Government a purer Naphtha, free of colour, in place of the tinted Naphtha as they at present receive and which occasions the discoloration of the Methylated Spirit. It is hoped that this application be successful and that in future we may receive Methylated Spirit of sufficient clearness and purity to do away with the necessity of redistillation

During the quarter the Number of Visitors has been

Ordinary —— 2049.
Medical Students 21
Total 2070.

The Conduct of the doorkeeper is satisfactory he is very attentive to his duties

Sigd. Wm. R. Sanders M.D.
Conservator.

1861.

First quarterly meeting of the Curators of the Museum.

Dr. P.H. Watson having signified his intention of resigning the office of Secretary to the Curators, the meeting proceeded to provide a successor, and Dr. Scoresby-Jackson was elected to the vacant office.

The following is a list of Curators for the current years.

Ex Off. Professor Syme.
Professor Miller.
Ordinary, Joseph Lister.
Patrick H. Watson, M.D.
Henry D. Littlejohn, M.D.
Alex. Mackenzie Edwards.
David Wilson, M.D.
Thomas Williamson, M.D.
William Walker.
R.E. Scoresby-Jackson, M.D. (Secretary).
James Spence.
John Burn, M.D.

The meeting resolved:- That the report of the Conservator of the Museum be embodied in the ordinary quarterly

Extract from Museum Committee Minute Book 1859-80.

The Watson Weymss Collection

'In accordance with the request of the Curators the Conservator has examined the preparations contained in the case of the workroom and has to report as follows – These preparations consist of – the collection of preparations of Dr Watson Weymss

Alexander Watson Wemyss (1799-1879).

... In consequence of communications made to Dr Watson Weymss, requesting him either to present this collection to the College or to remove it, the Curators are aware that Dr Watson Weymss has presented formally these preparations to the College... these specimens have been put in order and refitted and placed in the Museum as follows

96 preparations of the Eye – arranged on the shelves in Compartment No.IV, A North side of the long room

78 pathological preparations – also specimens representing medical jurisprudence – placed in a case fitted up for the purpose in compartment XXXVI of the Gallery.'

Museum Committee Minutes,
25th January 1869.

Alexander Watson Wemyss (1799-1879), or Alexander Watson (he adopted the additional surname Wemyss, his mother's maiden name, later in life) was the joint Keeper of the museum with Robert Hamilton from 1823-26 and had accompanied Robert Knox to London in 1825 to assess Charles Bell's collection. He had particular interests in Forensic Pathology and Ophthalmology (study of the eye) and he published several important books covering both subjects. In 1834 Watson Wemyss founded the Edinburgh Eye Infirmary.

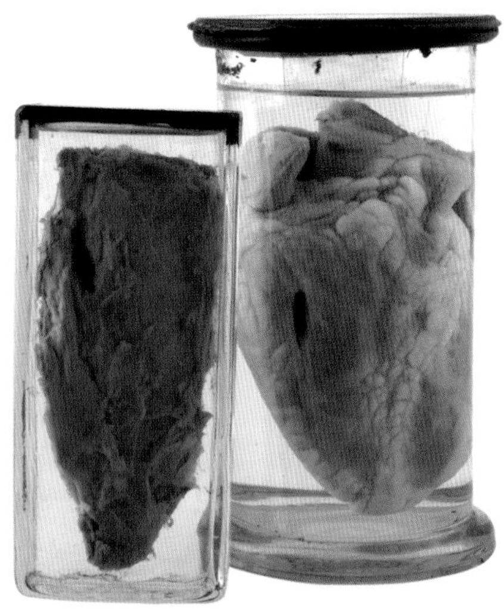

Forensic material resulting from the murder of a cobbler's wife by her husband in Edinburgh in 1830. Watson published the details of this and other murders he had been involved in investigating in *Homicide by External Violence*, 1837. GC 2277.

Shoemaker's knife, pierced skin and heart.

Original drawings by Alexander Watson (Weymss) published in *Dissections Illustrating the Anatomy of the Human Eye*, c. 1830. GCP 205.

The four top drawings of the eye ball were used as illustrations in Alexander Watson's *Anatomical Description of the Human Eye* published in 1828. All the drawings were used in the third edition of his *Compendium of the Diseases of the Human Eye* published in 1830 in which Watson notes: 'the drawings were made from preparations, which are still in my possession.'

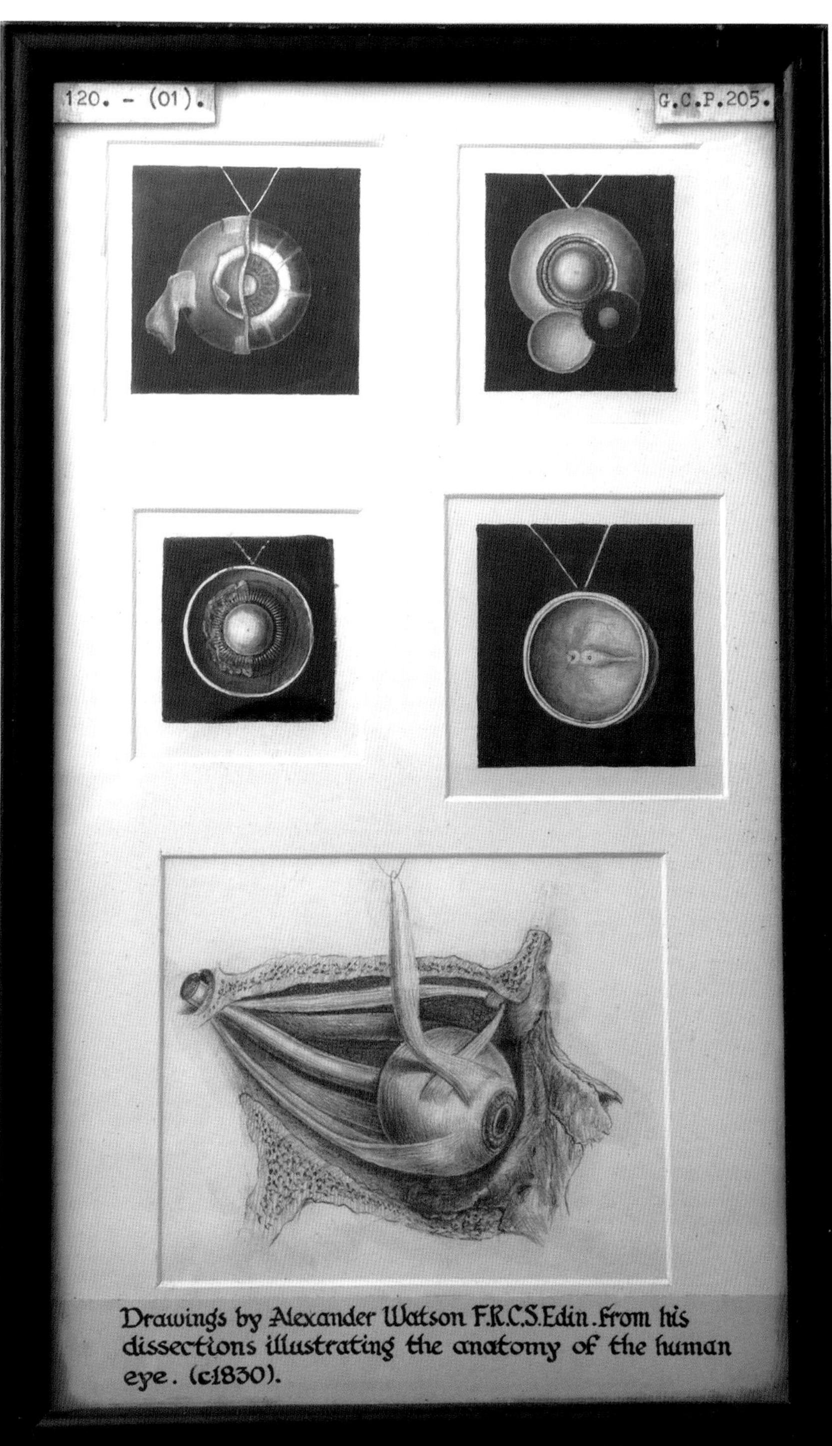
120. - (01).
G.C.P.205.
Drawings by Alexander Watson F.R.C.S.Edin. from his dissections illustrating the anatomy of the human eye. (c1830).

William Walker Collection

William Walker, Surgeon Oculist to Queen Victoria and first specialist ophthalmic surgeon appointed to the Royal Infirmary Edinburgh, was a curator of the museum from 1859 to 1864. He was President of RCSEd from 1871 to 1873.

In addition to Watson Weymss' collection further specimens, models and instruments connected to eye surgery were donated by William Walker (1814-1885) in the 1880s. As a result, by the end of the nineteenth century, the Museum collection had an exceptional strength in ophthalmology.

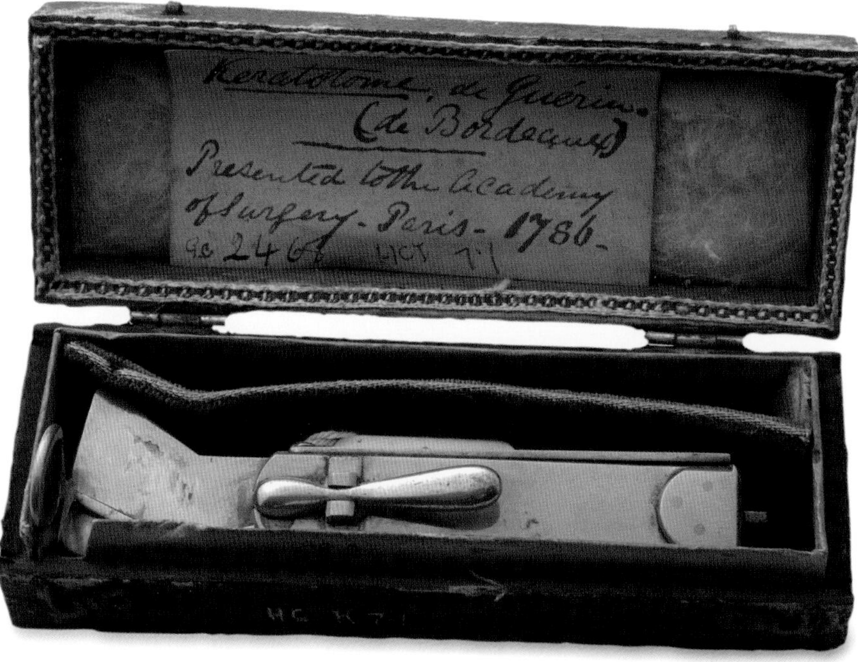

Eighteenth century French cataract instrument donated by William Walker. HC K 7.1.

To the Eye Surgeon

JOHN BURNSIDE

'my eyes have seen what my hand did'

– Robert Lowell

No matter what we say, we still believe
the soul is here, a live daguerrotype
recoiling from the laser's perfect stare:

the woods at daybreak, rain-light, mother love,
preserved intact, behind the tarnished shapes
you study and repair, with craft and guile;

though what you see is anaesthesia,
the opposite of space, antithesis
of childhood snow, or torchlight in the stars;

what you see is how the tissue looks
when things fall silent in the inner rooms
of blood and mind

– and how else would you work, if not
with something like suspended animation,
the windows shuttered on an empty house,

a random map of old iritis scars
and shadows on a damaged retina
the ghost companions of your healing eye?

No one should have to peer into the quick
of one soul, then another, through a haze
of cataracts and retinal decay;

the soul, when it is visible at all,
should always be a glimmer in the green,
a hidden thing, part-animal, part-stain,

shifting away, to weather long ago
forgotten, in a house of sleet and smoke,
beyond this work, beyond this field of vision.

Come fill up your cups & your glasses again
Like this philosophical medical man
I'll sing you a snatch of a song if I can
Of the Royal College of Surgeons

Chorus.

For there's many a pickle in Jar & in pot
The Examining fogies there have got
And they want you to know the devil knows what
At the Royal College of Surgeons

Chorus.

From the plantar arch to the circle of Willis
Above & below you'll have to show it
'Twill make a vast difference if you don't know it
When at the College of Surgeons

Chorus.

What makes up the ganglion of Meckel I pray
How much Carbon does anyone breathe in a day
Oh that's the style they whipper away
At the Royal College of Surgeons.

The Conan Doyle Connection

Arthur Conan Doyle was born in Edinburgh and studied medicine in the city between 1876 and 1881. His studies and the people who taught him were to influence his work for the rest of his life. It was Joseph Bell, a surgeon and lecturer in Clinical Surgery at the Royal Infirmary of Edinburgh, famed for his skill at diagnosing patients' conditions, who was to provide the inspiration for Conan Doyle's 'scientific detective' Sherlock

Bell was a curator of the museum from 1864 to 1869 and was treasurer and secretary of the College during Conan Doyle's time as a medical student. He was President from 1887-89.

Poem about sitting an anatomy exam at the Royal College of Surgeons of Edinburgh written by Arthur Conan Doyle. From his clinical notebook when he was a medical student in Edinburgh, session 1879/80. The Pathology Museum is still used for examinations today. RCSEd Collections.

Arthur Conan Doyle graduating in medicine from the University of Edinburgh, 1881. ©The Arthur Conan Doyle Collection Lancelyn Green Bequest, Portsmouth City Council.

Joseph Bell (1837-1911). By permission of the Stisted family.

The Waller Collection

Another important influence on Conan Doyle's medical learning was Bryan Charles Waller (1853-1932), the Doyle family lodger, who had come to stay with them around 1875. Waller graduated in medicine in 1876 and became a Fellow of the Royal College of Surgeons of Edinburgh in 1879, nominated by Joseph Bell. He established a pathology collection at Edinburgh University and tutored Conan Doyle using specimens from his collection. In 1889 Waller donated an extensive pathology collection to Surgeons' Hall Museum. Conan Doyle was to use many medical references in his stories:

"Are you a doctor?" He turned his fierce dark eyes upon me as he asked this last question.

"Yes, I am," I answered.

"Then put your hand here," he said, with a smile, motioning with his manacled wrists towards his chest.

I did so; and became at once conscious of an extraordinary throbbing and commotion which was going on inside. The walls of his chest seemed to thrill and quiver as a frail building would do inside when some powerful engine was at work. In the silence of the room I could hear a dull humming and buzzing noise which proceeded from the same source.

"Why," I cried, "you have an aortic aneurism!"

The prisoner Jefferson Hope and Dr Watson in an exchange from *A Study in Scarlet*, a Sherlock Holmes mystery, by Sir Arthur Conan Doyle, 1887.

▲ **Aortic Aneurysms** from the collection of Dr Rutherford Haldane donated to the College museum by Bryan Waller in 1889, then named the Waller Collection. GC 3049, GC 3055, GC 2961. Rutherford Haldane had taught at the Edinburgh Medical School based at Surgeons' Hall.

▶ **Dermoid Cyst.** Dermoid cysts are caused by the growth of unused stem cells. They often show hair and teeth within the sac of the cyst and can grow in men or women. The specimen of a diamond cyst shows a tooth growing within the cyst wall. GC 2909.

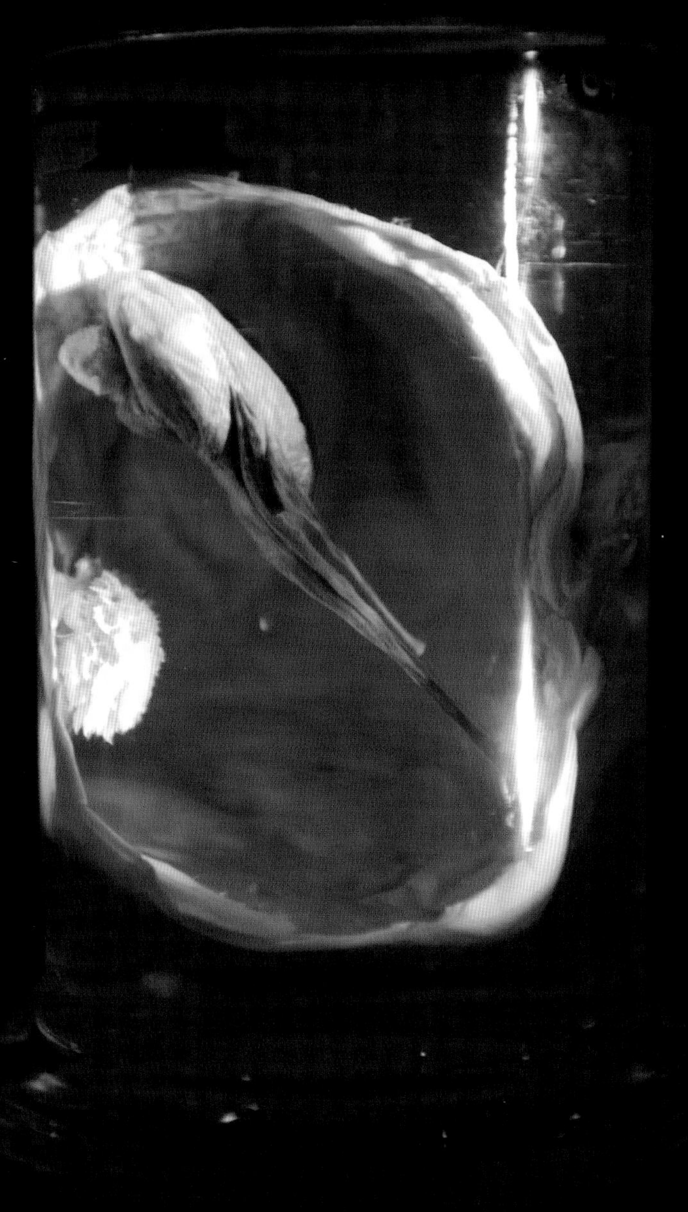

'Well if a single cell contains so much perhaps a single molecule and atom has more than we think. . . Have you ever had any personal experience of dermoid cysts?... You know that such cases are common enough in surgery, and that no pathological museum is without an example . . . But what are we to understand by it? So startling a phenomenon must have a deep meaning. That can only be, I think, that every cell in the body has the power latent in it by which it may reproduce the whole individual.'

Arthur Conan Doyle, *Round the Red Lamp, Being Facts and Fancies of Medical Life*, 1915.

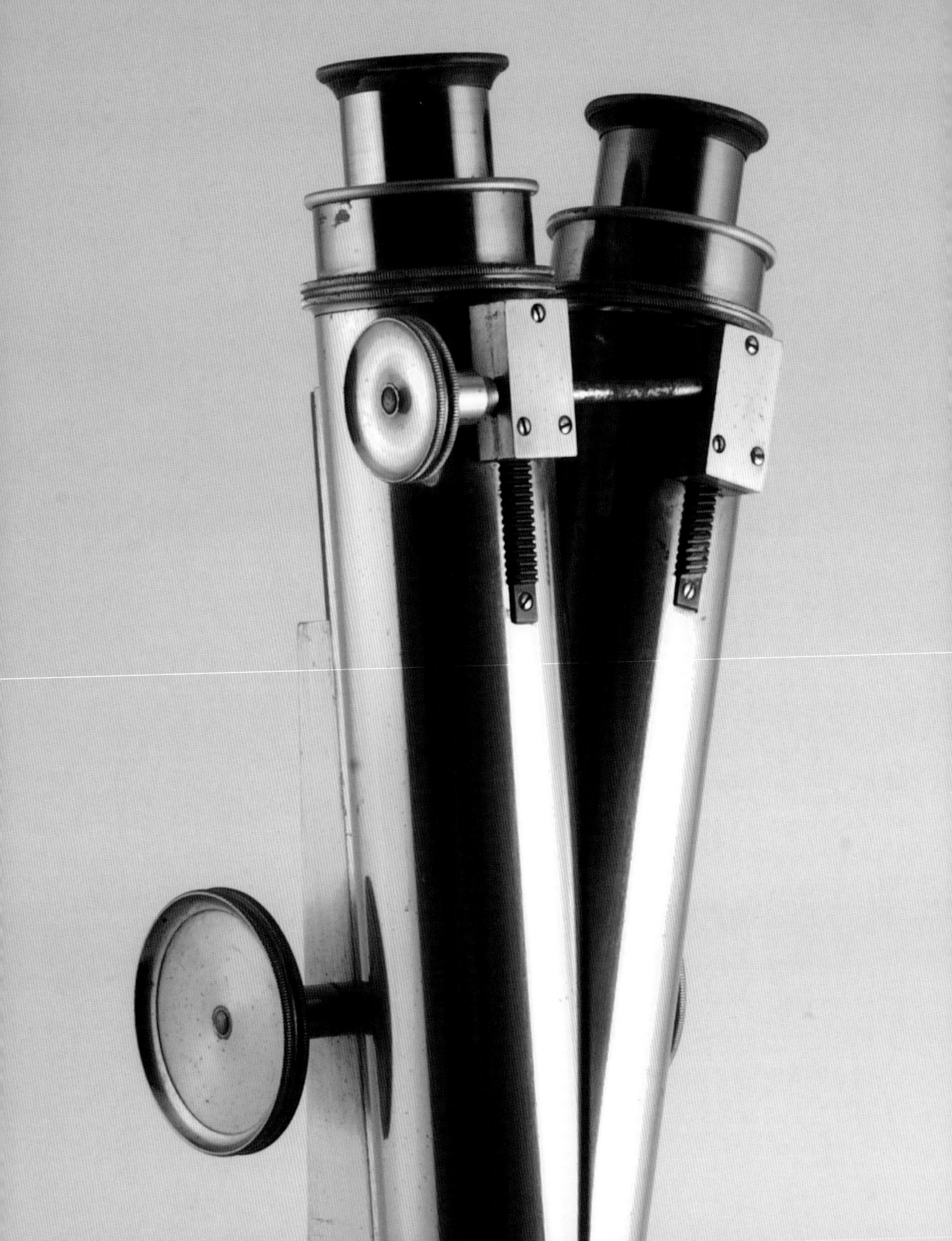

...for instruction and demonstrations

1887-1988

BECK BINOCULAR MICROSCOPE, 1866.
ON LOAN FROM THE NATIONAL MUSEUMS OF SCOTLAND.

Charles Walker Cathcart

The appointment in 1887 of Charles Cathcart (1853-1932) as conservator marked the beginning of significant modernisation of the museum, both in function and accommodation.

His belief that the museum was 'for instruction and demonstrations' led him to undertake an extensive redisplay of the collections, setting up a system more suited to modern teaching in pathology and surgery, complemented by a new three volume printed catalogue.

Cathcart also greatly enhanced the museums research facilities by establishing a museum laboratory in the tenement at 7 Hill Square, to the south east of the Playfair building. In 1902 a link 'bridge' was built between the two, joining for the first time the Pathology Museum with what is now the History of Surgery Museum.

Charles Walker Cathcart,
Museum Conservator 1887-1900.

Cathcart's Freezing Microtome, 1906.
In 1890 Cathcart decided that all examples of tumours in the museum collections should be examined microscopically. Slides were prepared by cutting small 'sections' from the specimens and slicing them, placing them between glass and then examining them under a microscope. Microtomes are used to slice and by freezing the section a cleaner cut could be achieved. Cathcart established a museum laboratory in 1897 primarily to carry out this work. HC.RA.1.1.

In his introduction to the *Descriptive Catalogue of the Anatomical and Pathological Specimens in the Museum of the Royal College of Surgeons of Edinburgh*, 1893, Cathcart writes:

'Formerly, in this as in many other Museums, spirit preparations were placed in one part of the Museum, dried preparations in another, casts in a third, and drawings in a fourth. Now, they are all classed together in the catalogue when they belong to the same or similar specimens. Where, owing to variations in shape and size, some of the individual members of a group could not be conveniently placed upon the shelves with the rest, every effort has been made to place them so close to the others that the student can refer to them without loss either of time, or of a sense of general continuity. In many cases published drawings of the patients from whom the specimens were taken have been copied by photography and placed beside the specimens they illustrate.'

The *Descriptive Catalogue of the Anatomical and Pathological Specimens of the Royal College of Surgeons of Edinburgh* known as the 'New Catalogue'. Volumes 1 and 2 by Charles Cathcart, 1893 and 1898. Volume 3 by Theodore Shennan, Cathcart's successor as Museum Conservator, 1902. The Museum shelves were arranged to correspond to the catalogue order, with specimens grouped in numbered series according to 'present views of pathology.'

The Struthers Collection

John Struthers (1823-1899) retired as Professor of Anatomy at Aberdeen University in 1889, a post he had held since 1863, and returned to Edinburgh where he had studied medicine and worked as a surgeon and teacher from the 1840s to the 1860s.

He was President of the College of Surgeons from 1895 to 1897 and during that time donated his private anatomy collection to the College. Struthers' collection is not only important because of it size, over 1600 specimens and casts, but because of the sources of his collection and his own distinctive methods of preservation. The original collection that he took with him to Aberdeen combined major parts of the collections of the famed anatomists: Peter Handyside (1808-1881), John Lizars (1787-1860) and Robert Knox. Struthers also added specimens from William MacGillivray's collection which he bought after MacGillivray's death in 1852. The Struthers collection creates a 'golden thread' from the1820s through to the 1890s, representing the work of five of Britain's most influential figures in the development of nineteenth century anatomy and natural history.

Struthers made many of his own preparations by injecting coloured wax into blood vessels to highlight their path and varnishing the specimens to prevent decay. GC 14141.

Dissection of a frog. Struthers Collection. GC 14089. Photo Andrew Connell.

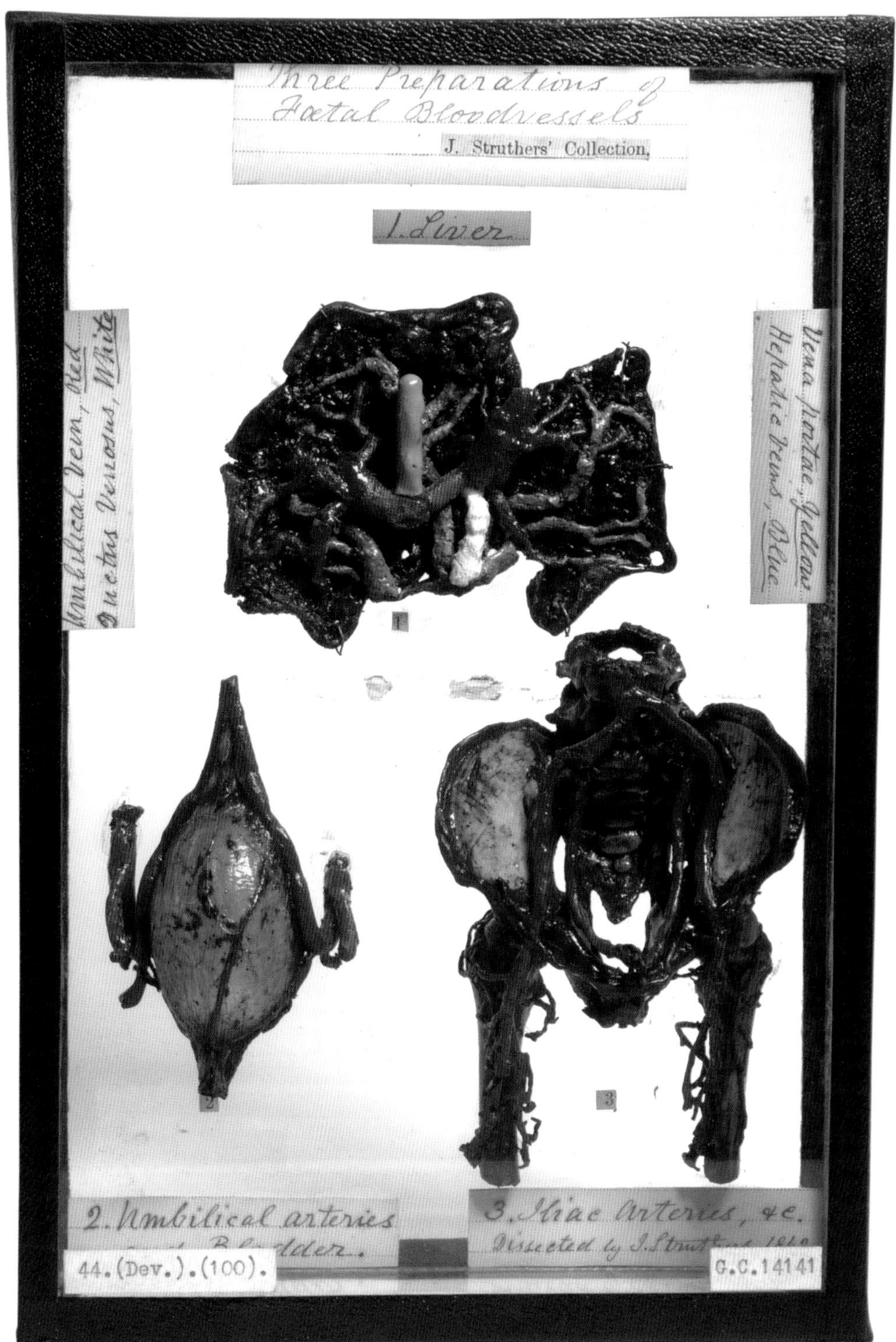

Three Preparations of
Fœtal Bloodvessels
J. Struthers' Collection.
1. Liver
Umbilical Vein, Red
Ductus Venosus, White
Vena Portae, Yellow
Hepatic Veins, Blue
1
2
3
2. Umbilical arteries
Bladder.
3. Iliac Arteries, &c.
44.(Dev.).(100).
G.C.14141

Henry Wade

The first decade of the 20th century saw significant changes in the internal accommodation at Surgeons' Hall. In 1907 the architect Arthur Balfour Paul was appointed to extend and convert the Barclay Museum into a new 'Main Hall' for meetings and ceremonial functions.

The Barclay Collection was moved to a new museum space created in the adjoining tenement in Hill Square, and modern surgical displays, to be used for demonstration, were added.

Royal College of Surgeons' Museum, Edinburgh.

Date 12. 1. 04.

No. 1.

Nature of Specimen Scirrhous Cancer of Breast.

Report on Specimen

Slide No. 1. Tumour 2. Gland.

History of Case

Donor Sir Patrick Heron Watson

General Catalogue No. not added

Henry (later Sir Henry) Wade (1876-1955), appointed conservator in 1903, oversaw the move of the museum collections and the design of the new displays. Wade, a surgeon specialising in urology, also added a large number of specimens of kidneys, ureters, bladders, prostates and urethras from his clinical work, enhancing the museum's collections and research in the field of urology.

▲ Henry Wade, Museum Conservator, 1903-20.

◀ **Scroll Books**
In 1907 Wade introduced a new system for entering museum specimens into the collection. The 'Scroll Books' were based on day books used in pathology laboratories, they had perforated pages with one part given as a receipt to the donor. This system was used until 2003 when international museum documentation standards were adopted.

▶ **Kidney specimen** presented by Henry Wade. This specimen shows a huge 'staghorn' calculus occupying the entire renal pelvis and calyces. GC 7478.

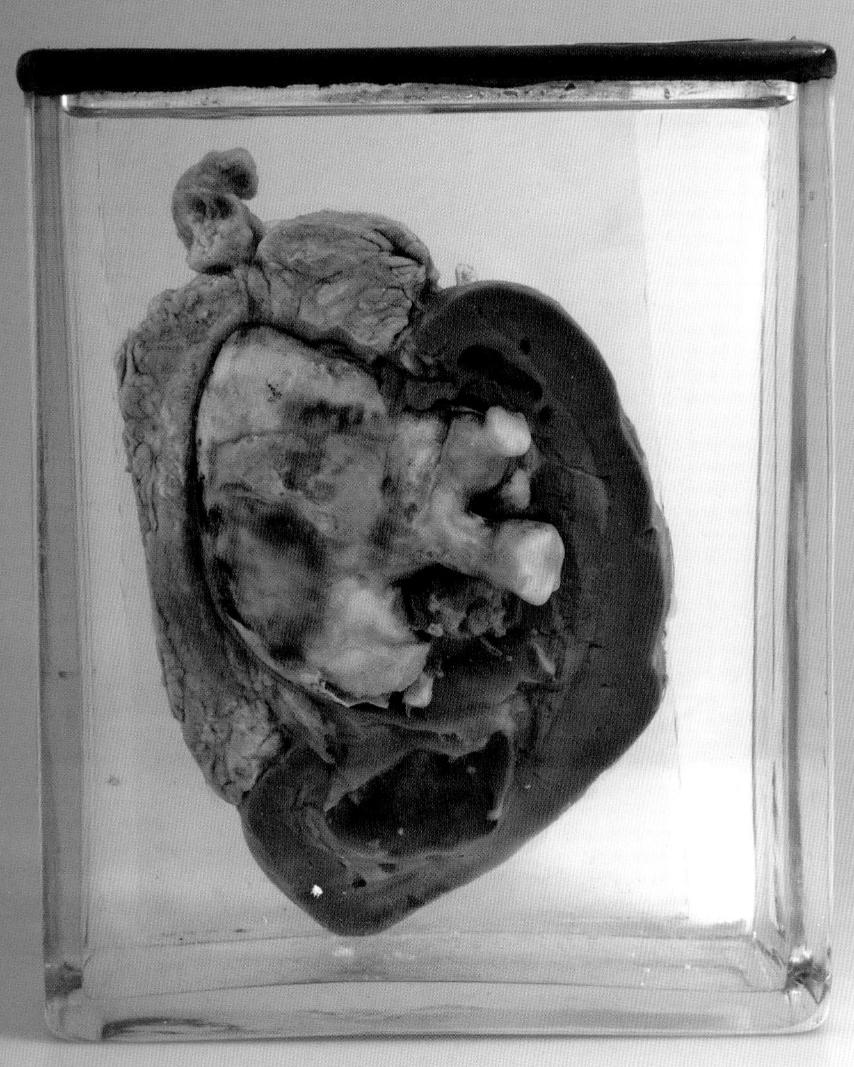

New Museum Hall 1909. The New Museum Hall was created from the two upper storeys of No 7 Hill Square and was opened In December 1909. It was later named the Cathcart Hall after Charles Cathcart, conservator until 1900. It now houses Surgeons' Hall's Museum of the History of Surgery. Courtesy of RCAHMS (Bedord Lemere Collection).

The John Barclay Room. The Barclay Room created in 1909 from the upper two storeys of No 9 Hill Square. In the early 1990s the ceiling was reinstated and the lower floor now houses the Menzies Campbell Dental Collection. Photo 1982 © RCAHMS.

World War One 1914-1918

The injury and disease suffered by millions of men and women in military service during World War One led to great changes in the practice of surgery. Experimentation with new weapons, including gas and aerial attack, required medical services to develop new treatments and methods of diagnosis of internal injury.

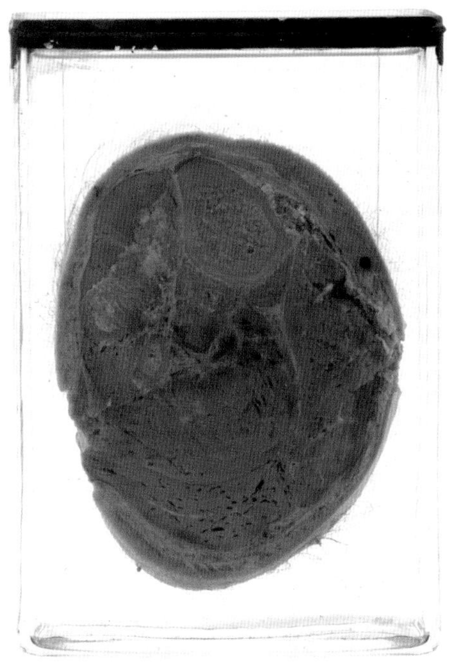

Many newly qualified doctors were hurried into theatres of war, receiving their surgical training 'on the job' in frontline battlefield hospitals. Some of these hospitals also established laboratories with collections of human tissue showing the effect of wounds and disease.

After the war some of these specimens, often showing shocking wounds, were brought back and donated to the museum by medical staff, keen they should be used for teaching future generations of surgeons.

▲ **Gas gangrene.** Section of leg showing gas gangrene from soldier wounded c1916. Gas gangrene is caused by the infection of a wound from bacteria often found in rich soil, such as the heavily cultivated fields on the French Western Front in World War One. GC 7757.

◀ **Gunshot wound**
A portion of the face showing a gunshot wound of the nose and left upper eyelid, from a soldier wounded in France, March, 1917. The wound, which has been carefully sutured, passes from the right side of the nose across the nasal bridge. GC 7878.

The Greig Collection

David Middleton Greig (1864 - 1936), Conservator of the Museum from 1920 to 1936, was an international authority on bone disease and abnormalities of the skull. During his professional life as a surgeon, in and around his home city of Dundee, he formed his own pathology collection, documenting every case in detail and adding photographs, X-rays and drawings.

David Middleton Greig in 1917.

The Pathology Museum c 1914 - 1926.
This photograph appears in Clarendon Creswell's *The Royal College of Surgeons of Edinburgh Historical Notes from 1505 to 1905*. Creswell, the College sub-librarian, was called up for military service in 1914 and was killed in action in October 1918. His book was published posthumously in 1926. It is not known if this photograph was taken before Creswell left to fight in World War One.

Greig published extensively on surgery, mental deficiency, the surgical pathology and syndromes of bone and gave his name to two syndromes: Greig's Cephalosyndactyly Syndrome (Greig I) and Greig's Ocular Hypertelorism Syndrome (Greig II). He donated his collection, which included over 250 skulls, to the Museum.

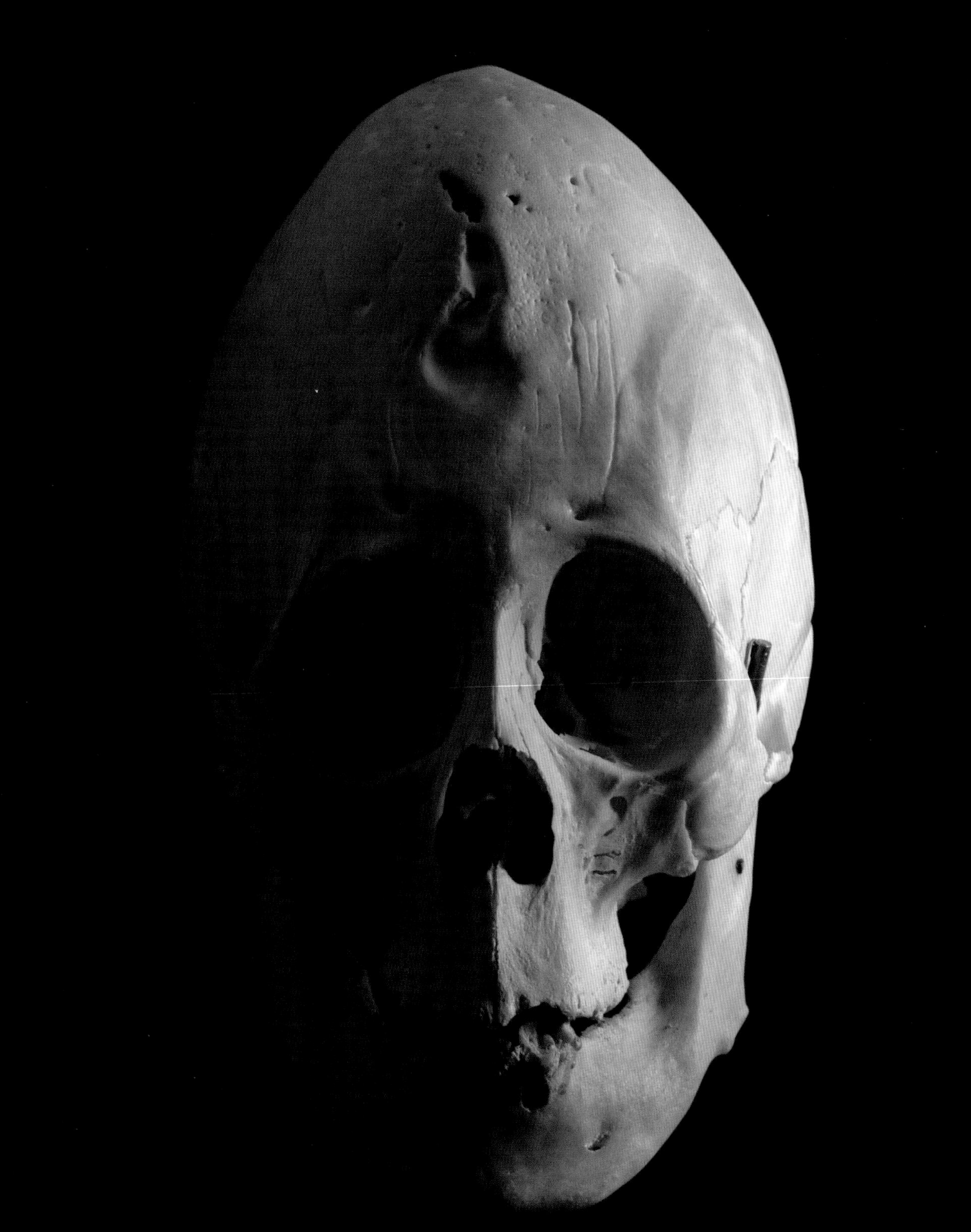

Greig's notes recorded: *'Oxycephaly. A sixty-two year old female with a massive skull related to premature fusion of the coronal and sagittal sutures (synostosis) had associated malformations of the hands and feet (syndactyly). She was of normal intelligence. The oxycephalic deformity was caused by premature fusion of two principal sutures in the skull which led to a tower shaped skull. The shape of the skull was related to the growth of the brain which allowed it to grow where the sutures were still open. Later in life when growth had ceased these fused together.'* GC 9644.

Hypertelorism. In 1924 Greig was the first to describe orbital hypertelorism, a rare condition leading to wide separation of the eyes and arrested development of the greater wings of the sphenoid (the wedge shaped bone at the base of the skull). The condition is also called Greig's (II) Syndrome. GC 5496.

Stereolithographic models of skulls. Modern treatment of hypertelorism involves surgery to reduce the distance between the eye sockets and to correct nasal abnormalities. In advance of the operation a model of the patient's skull is made in an acrylic material using 3D scans. Another model is made to show how the bone might be reconstructed through surgery and allows the surgeon the chance to 'rehearse' the operation and visualise the best outcome in advance. RCSEd Collections.

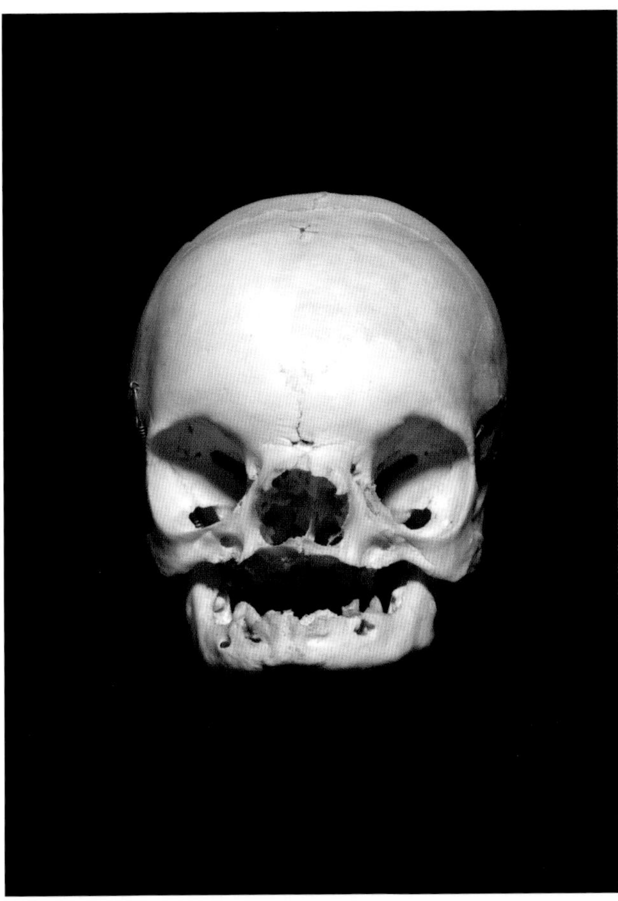

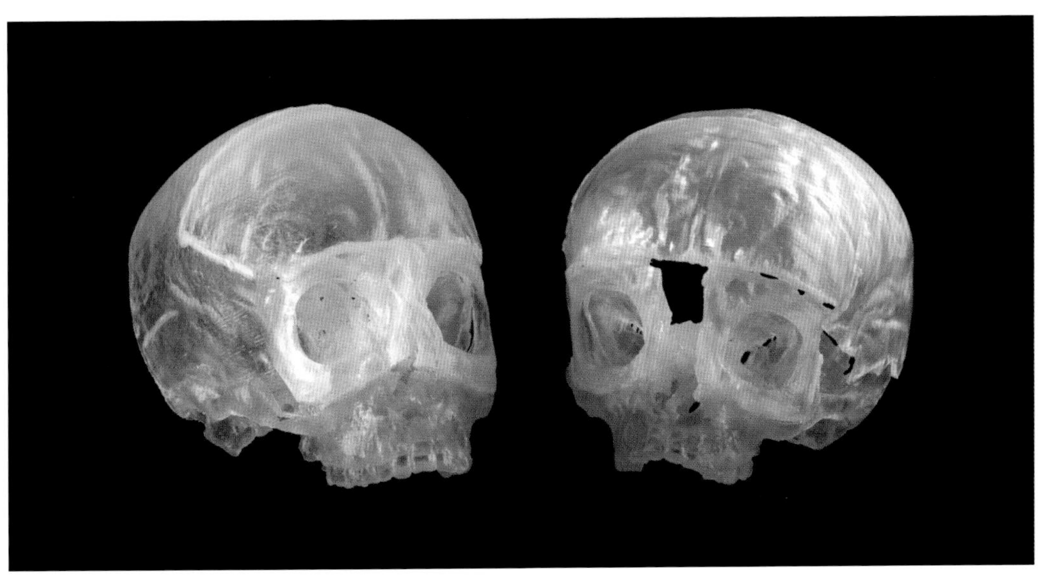

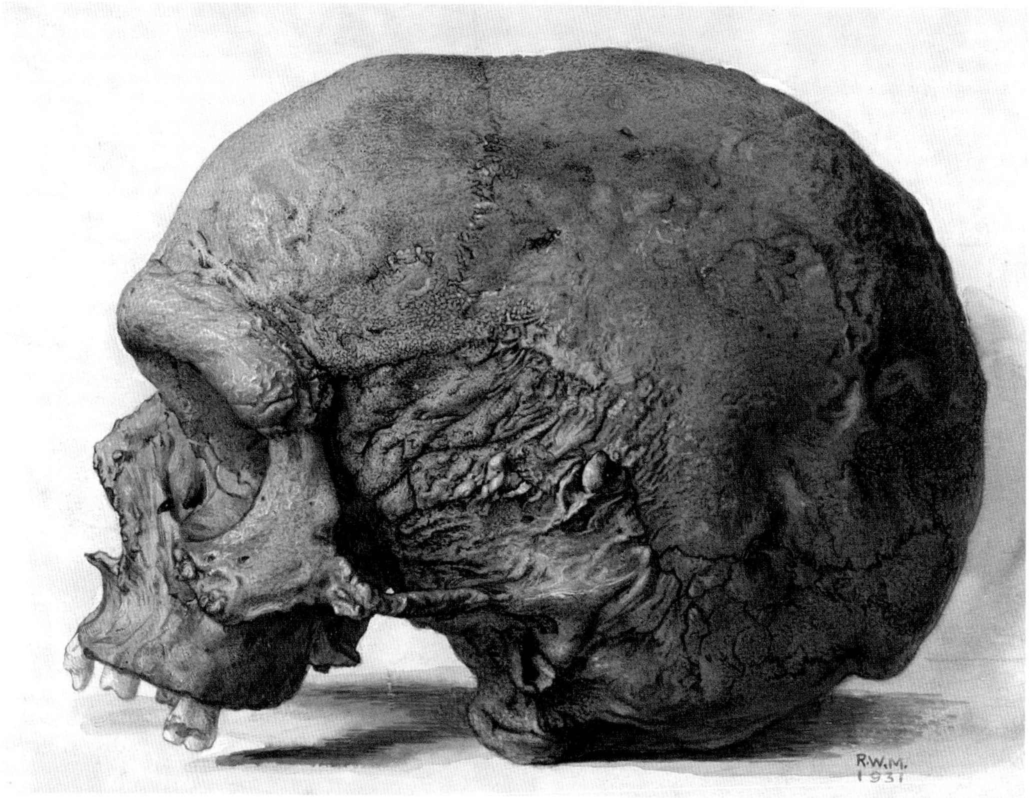

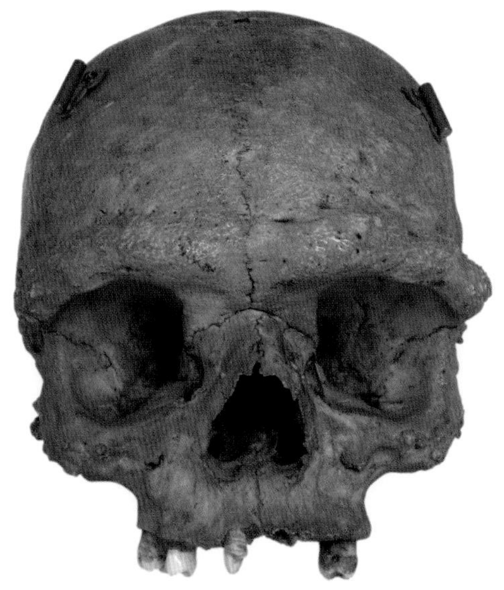

▲ **Adult Neanderthaloid skull showing malformation**, 1931 by Robert Wilson Matthews RSA (1880 - 1940). Photo Max McKenzie.

◀ **Adult Neanderthaloid skull**, Greig Collection, GC 941.3. Photo Max McKenzie.

▶ **Museum Assistant William Waldie in the Barclay Room** c. late 1920s. The Barclay Collection had been moved from its original accommodation in the Playfair building in 1909. The new Barclay Room was created from two upper flats at No 9 Hill Square. Some of Greig's skull collection is on display in the cabinet behind Waldie, the door on the left led through to the Museum Laboratory established in 1897.

World War Two (1939-45)

On the outbreak of World War Two the museum conservatorship passed from Charles Illingworth to John William Struthers, then College Treasurer and Secretary, and President from 1941 to 1943.

For fear of damage by enemy air raids the museum specimens were moved to the basement areas of Surgeons' Hall until 1943. During the War the museum was staffed by just one man, James (Jimmy) Jack supported by the College Officer James Smith. Jack worked as the museum technical assistant from 1921 to 1964. He was the longest serving member of the museum staff.

▲ **John W Struthers,** Museum Conservator 1939-1947.

◀ **Jimmy Jack,** Museum Technician 1921-1964.

Post War

James Norman Jackson Hartley took up duties as conservator in 1947. New museum staff, including a secretary and a laboratory technician, were appointed in the same year and the College Museum was once again open to the public.

In 1948 changes in medical education brought an end to undergraduate teaching at the College of Surgeons and Hartley began developing the collection to make it more useful for modern postgraduate study. His approach was based on the study of pathological material in conjunction with clinical aspects of a case (surgical pathology, living pathology): incorporating full clinical details in the records of all new specimens.

New museum accommodation was created in 1953 at 4 Hill Square, adjacent to the Cathcart Hall; it included a new laboratory, photographic facilities, a demonstration room and a workshop for making perspex containers for mounting specimens.

Castle Street.
Signet and S.S.C. Library, Parliament Square. Order from Members.
Stevenson Memorial House and Museum, 8 Howard Place, Summer, 10 A.M. to 5 P.M.; Winter, 10 A.M. to 4 P.M.; admission, 6d.
Stevenson Cottage, Swanston.
Stone of Remembrance, Royal Exchange, High St.
Surgeons' Hall Museum, Nicholson Street, Monday, Wednesday, 12 to 4; Saturday, 10 to 1; free.
University (South Bridge), daily, 10 A.M. to 1 P.M.; Saturday, 10 A.M. to 12 NOON.
Usher Hall, Lothian Road.
Wellington Monument, Princes St. (facing G.P.O.).
Zoological Gardens, Corstorphine Road, 9 A.M. to 7 P.M. Monday to Friday, 1s., Children, 6d. Saturday, 9d., Children, 4d. Sunday (after 1 P.M.), 1s., Children, 6d.

1947 Edinburgh Tram Guide. Surgeons' Hall Museum is featured in 'Places of Interest' as open free of charge: Monday, Wednesday and Saturday.

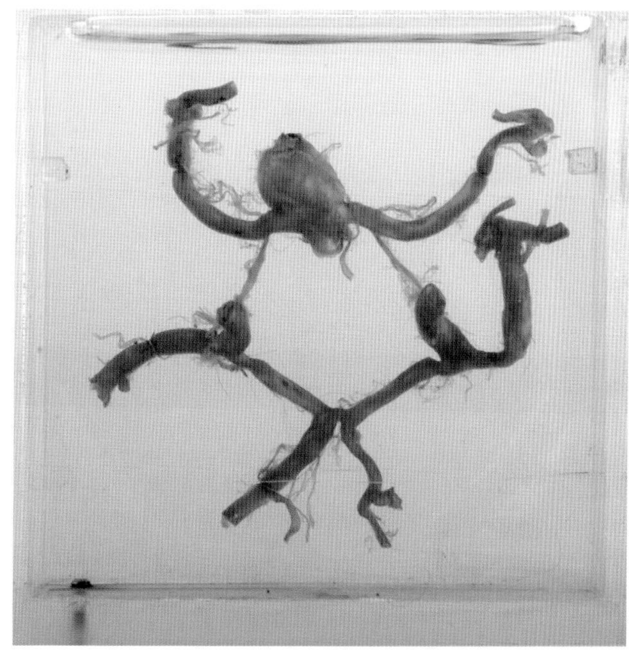

Circle of Willis. In 1953 new facilities at the museum led to the production of Perspex containers for mounting specimens replacing the older practice of using glass jars. GC 8118a.

Eric Mekie

David Eric Cameron Mekie's (1902-1989) conservatorship saw great changes in the content and display of the museum collections. Although much of the Barclay collection was disposed of in the mid 1950s several important new collections, including dentistry, histology and radiology, were added during Mekie's time.

In the early 1960s a new emphasis was given to the display of historical artefacts in the museum collections prompting many Fellows and their relatives to donate personal objects and archives connected to the history of surgery.

Mekie made a huge contribution to the development of the museum, enhancing its use for postgraduate study. He continued to be active in the affairs of the museum after his retirement as conservator producing two volumes of an extensive atlas of the collections and co-authoring with Mrs Violet Tansey, the full-time museum secretary and administrator from 1972 to 1995, a valuable history of the museum.

The Cathcart Hall with displays showing historical objects, c.1975.

Violet Tansey and Eric Mekie at the launch of *A Colour Atlas of Demonstrations in Surgical Pathology Vols 1 and 2*, edited by Eric Mekie. 1983.

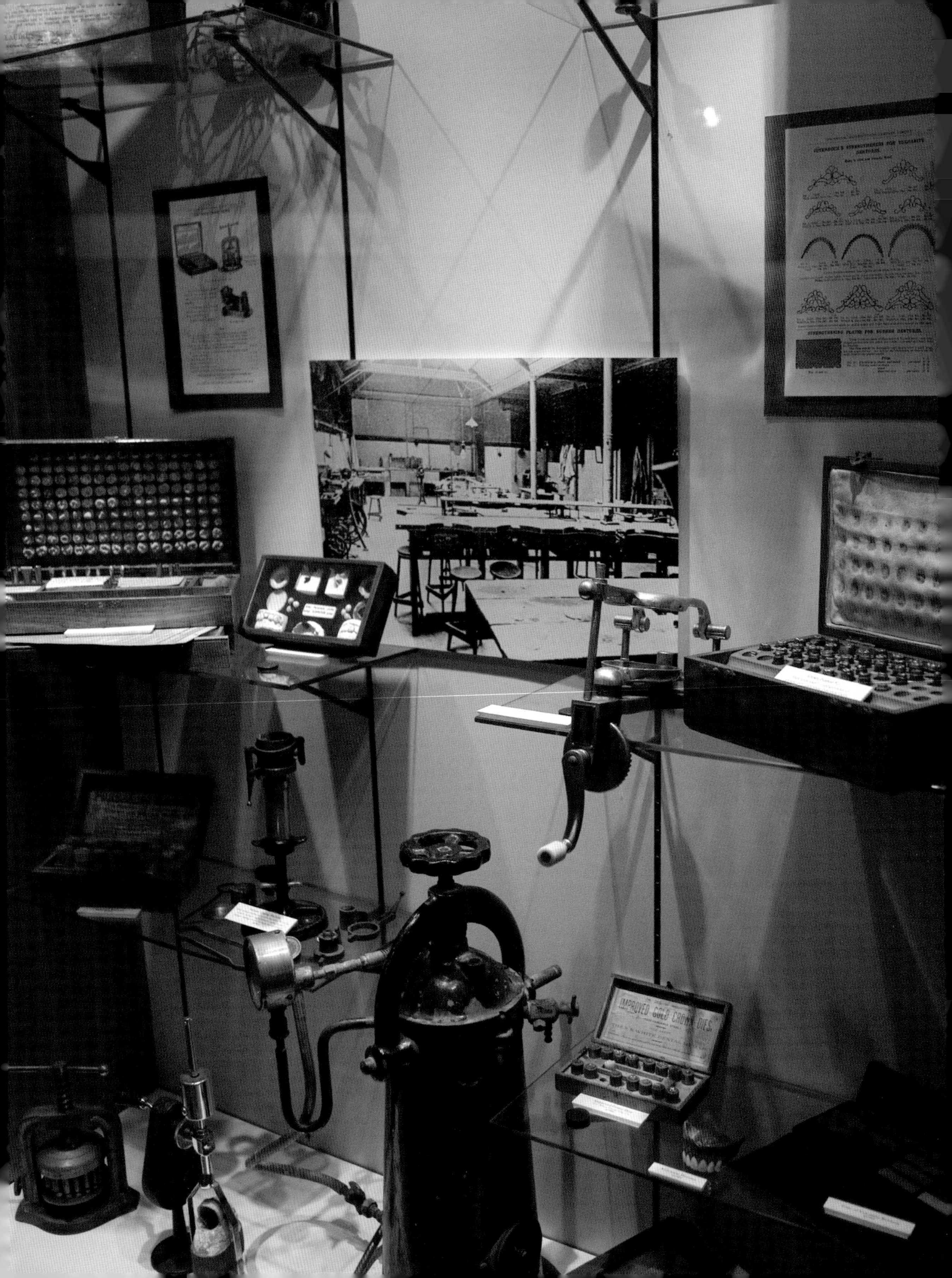
IMPROVED GOLD CROW
DIES.

The Menzies Campbell Collection

'Your College is the cradle of Scottish dentistry. Many of the 18th and 19th century Fellows laid solid foundations for the dissemination of knowledge on the anatomy, physiology and disease of the teeth.

John Menzies Campbell (1887-1974) was a Scottish dentist and eminent dental historian. He donated his collection to the College in 1965. It, with the other donations made since the 1860s is rated as one of Britain's most important dental collections.

Display Case, Menzies Campbell Collection, c1995. Photo Max McKenzie.

Paul Geissler was appointed first Dental Collection Conservator in 1994.

Further, your College is the only one in Britain or in Ireland which has ever elected as its President a surgeon who restricted his practice to dental surgery. I refer to Francis Brodie Imlach who was in office from 1883 to 1885, and John Smith from 1883 to 1885... who realised the inadequacy of lectures without clinical instruction. As an outcome, in 1860, he along with Robert Naysmith, Imlach and others opened the Dental Dispensary...Your College, ever in the vanguard, was, in 1895, the first in Britain to admit a woman Licentiate in Dental Surgery.

... For many years I have been perplexed over a problem which, sooner or later, besets every collector – namely, which body should be entrusted with the care and preservation of the various items which have been assembled over the years...On learning of your College's willingness to ensure adequate accommodation for permanent display, I straightaway decided that this was the ideal place.

The very attractively planned, the superbly designed cases and the admirable appointed display have merely strengthened my opinion. I can only trust that the collection will form a helpful and practical educational asset to your College and encourage dental surgeons and students of to-day and tomorrow to study our history – a most intriguing and rewarding pursuit.

I have never seen a dental collection so attractively presented or to such advantage...To Professor Mekie and his technicians I would say: Thank you very much indeed.'

JOHN MENZIES CAMPBELL reply to the President of RCSEd on the opening of the Menzies Campbell Collection. Surgeons' Hall, 30th June 1965.

Harrington's Clockwork 'Erado' Drill, 1864.
Menzies Campbell Collection. HC J.7.x.5.

Der Zahnarzt by unknown artist.
Late 18th century, after the painting by Gerrit Dou (1613-75). HCJ 16x61.

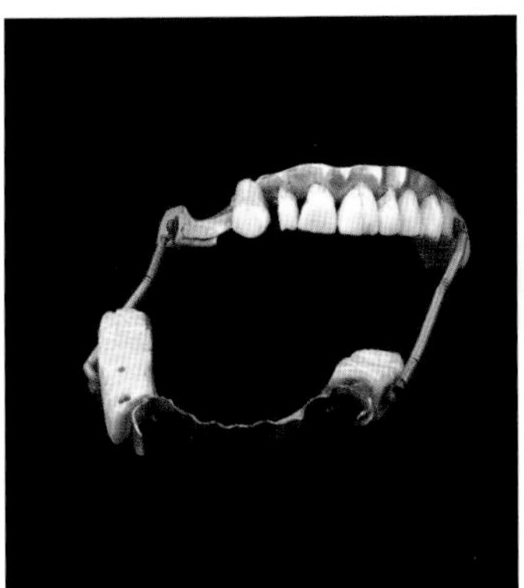

Upper and lower dentures. Gold base, ivory block posterior teeth, c.1820. RCSEd Collections.

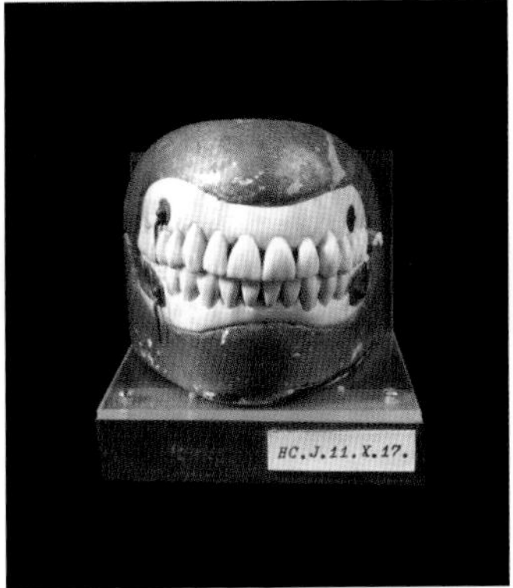

Upper and lower dentures, mid 19th century. Menzies Campbell Collection, RCSEd Collections HC.J. 11.17.

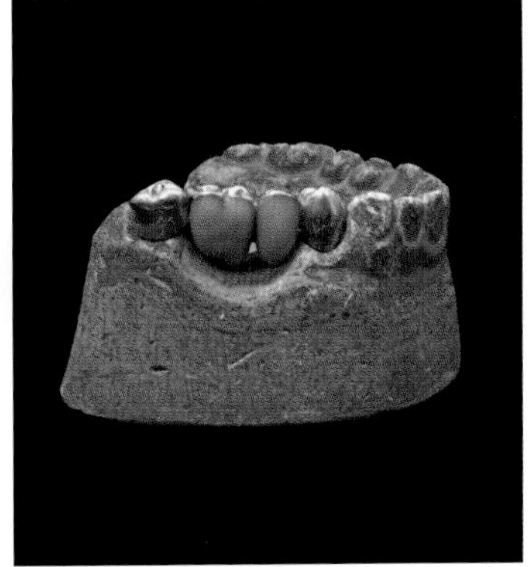

Fixed moveable bridge and skeleton partial denture base, 1901. SB 24/1146.

Second Tooth

ELIZABETH BURNS

The first one came out the week of her birthday.
This second tooth's harder: she pushes
and pushes at it with her tongue, tries to grip and drag it out.
Nothing comes but blood.

In the museum is the jawbone of a child, undated.
A label in fine ink: *Upper and Lower Milk Teeth*
and first permanent molar.
You can see the next loose milk tooth,
jutting squintly from the lower jaw.
Nobody dislodged it when the child died,
nobody kept that little white seed-pearl.
They left the mouth as it was, when its tongue
could wiggle the wobbly tooth,
and there was almost a gap in the grin.

At the school gate she's clutching the tooth
in a paper towel. It fell out at playtime
just when she'd finished her apple and milk.
That night she wraps it in tissue
puts it under her pillow
with a note for the fairy not to take it away.
In the morning, a shining twenty-pence piece
that she puts with the tooth in her heart-shaped box.
Inside her mouth, the permanent molars,
the teeth of an adult, are pushing and pushing through.

Anatomical preparation showing upper and lower milk teeth. SB 24/170. RCSEd Collections.

Edith Dawson

The pathologist Dr Edith Dawson was appointed to the Museum staff in 1961 to undertake diagnostic histology for Fellows of the College. She also began research on museum specimens and donated her own large collection of histological material relating to breast disease to the museum.

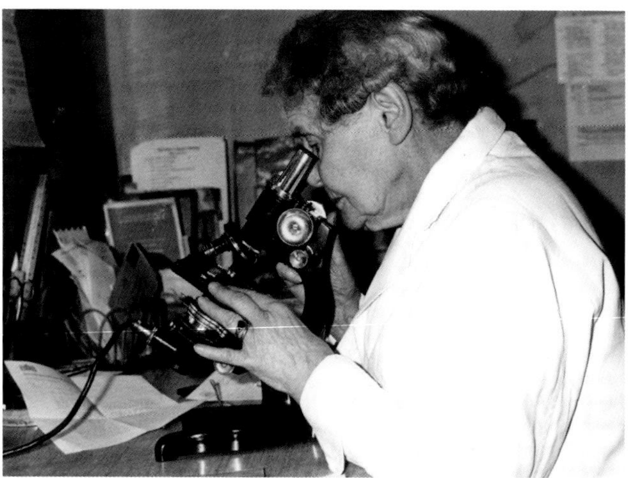

◀ Edith Dawson (1886-1983).

▼ **Illustration of histopathology** made by Dr James Dawson (1870-1927), Edith Dawson's husband. James Dawson was a recipient of the Syme Fellowship in Surgery (1910), but devoted much of his life to histology and research into the pathological nature of tumours and other tissues. The illustrations show new bone formation and malignant giant cell tumour of femur.

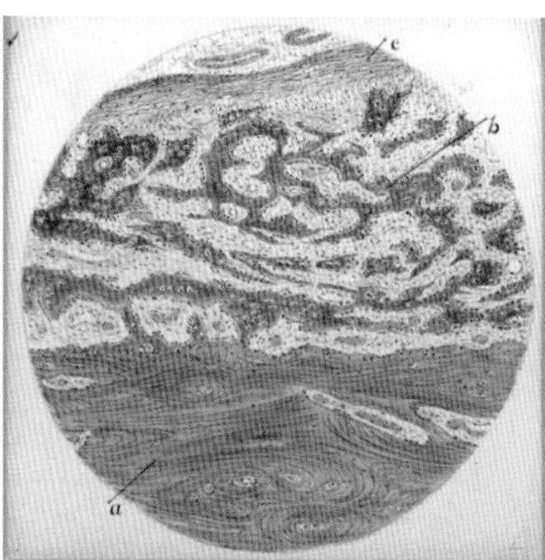

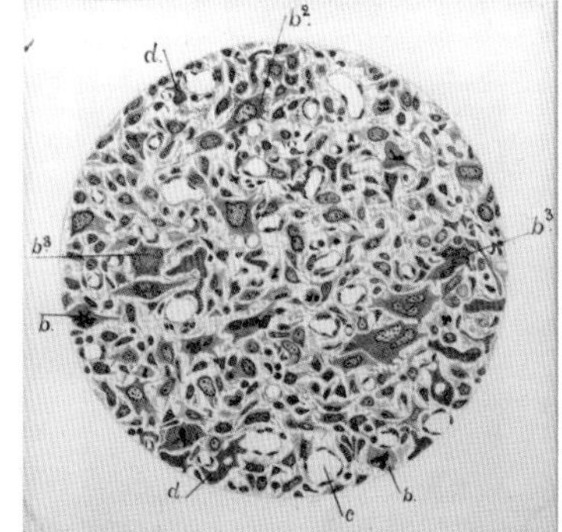

Radiology Collection

In 1971 Scotland's first radiological collection was begun at Surgeons' Hall by Dr Bill Copland. A bequest from the estate of Mr Bruce M Dick covered the cost of adapting the old museum workshop and staff room into a dedicated space for the new X-ray collection with viewing equipment, donated by Kodak.

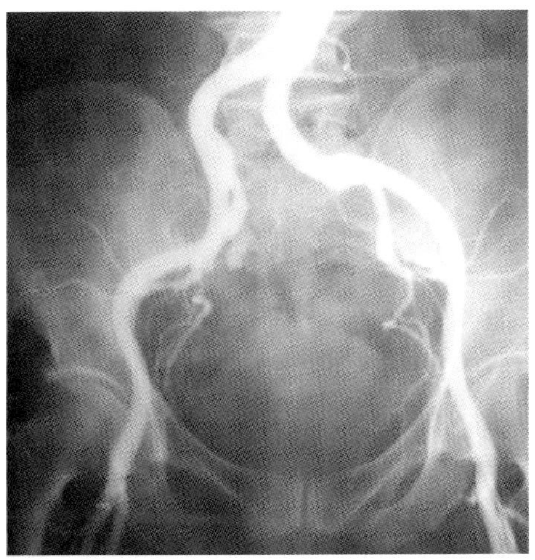

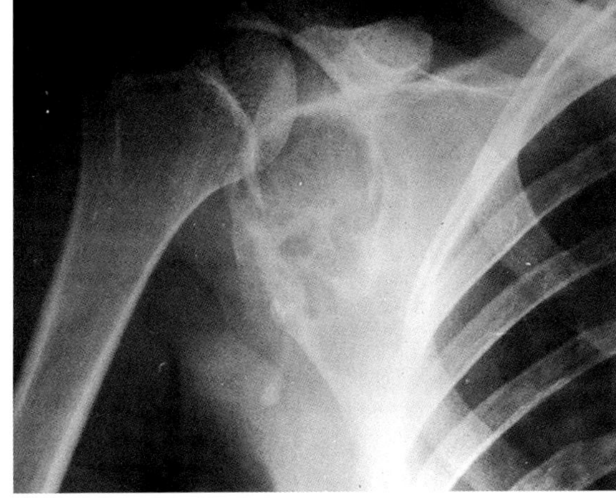

X-rays from Surgeons Hall Radiology Collection.

▲ Arteriogram showing Arteriosclerosis. GCX 687.

◥ Aneurysmal bone cyst of scapula. GCX 182.

▶ Intravenous urogram showing contrast in both renal collecting systems. Gallstones are present in the gall bladder and common bile duct. GCX 77.

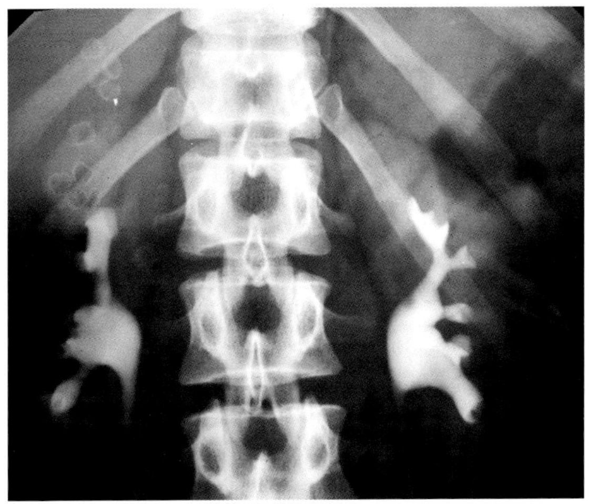

...valued by the public

1989-2009

BLOOD VESSELS, HAND, INJECTED WITH RED LEAD. DONATED BY ROBERT LISTON. RCSED COLLECTIONS.

Valued by the Public…

At the opening of Surgeons' Hall, in 1832, John Gairdner, the President of the College, said that he hoped the museum would be 'valued by the public.' His hope was certainly realised: for most of its history the annual number of visits by members of the public has exceeded those by a medical audience.

By the 1970s public access was restricted to occasional pre booked group tours, but with an ever declining use of the museum for modern surgical teaching it was recognised that the public audience was an important one.

In 1982 the College supported the recommendation of the museum committee to develop a more comprehensive museum of the history of surgery in Scotland, built on the foundations of the historical displays from Eric Mekie's conservatorship. The displays were to map the history of the College from 1505 and highlight the work and achievements of some of its most famous members and museum conservators.

The Official Opening of the Surgeons' Hall Museum of the History of Surgery, July 1989. Pictured left to right. Geoffrey Chisholm, President of RCSEd; Mrs Rylands, daughter of Jules Thorn and Dr Alistair Masson, Honorary Archivist of RSCEd.

Surgeons' Hall Museum of the History of Surgery.

The project was made viable by substantial funds from the Jules Thorn Trust and a grant from the Scottish Museums Council. From December 1990 the museum was open to the public on Tuesdays and Thursdays from 2 - 4pm.

Anna
CAST FROM NATURE 1845
JOHN GOODSIR

Apothecary's Mortar
A replica of a mortar belonging to Gilbert Primrose, Deacon (president) of the Incorporation of Surgeons (1581). The original, in the Museum of Scotland, is thought to have been lost by Primrose in 1558 when he was on military duty 'for the defence of the towne' against 'our auld inemyes of Ingland'. It was unearthed by a ploughman in the Scottish Borders at the end of the 19th century. Mortars were used by surgeon apothecaries to crush plant extracts. RCSEd Collections.

Bleeding Bowl
Blood can be taken from many sites on the body but the large antecubital vein of the arm was considered one of the easiest. Blood was collected in bowls made from silver, pewter or ceramics. At first smooth-sided, bowls came to be designed with indents to match the curvature of the arm. RCSEd Collections.

Head: Sabre Wound

VALERIE GILLIES

The strokes of a sabre
on his wan head –
those blows repeated
in the heat
of battle
where sabres whirl
like flames.

An attack
by a tiger
or the wake
of a cutlass?
He is conscious
but he can't speak.

Better the clean cut
of the sabre than all
the musket-fire, grape-shot
or tearaway cannonball.

A field surgeon knows
such a head injury
gives 'frequent opportunities
of seeing the upper
and the lateral parts
of the cerebrum
exposed
by sabre wounds.'

To manoeuvre a cavalry horse
ridden in balance
staying steady
always
leaving the sabre arm free
is a skill
parried by another:
to remove fragments of bone
from the skull
allowing the wounded
dragoon
to recover.

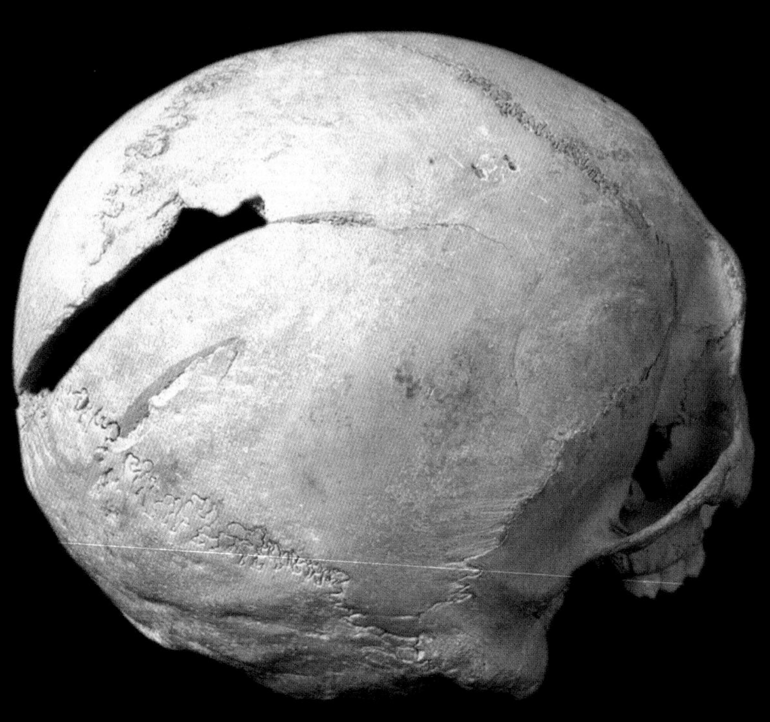

Set of surgical instruments, early 19th century. Field surgical set of instruments used during the Napoleonic Wars. Instruments include an amputation saw, knives and tourniquet. RCSEd Collections.

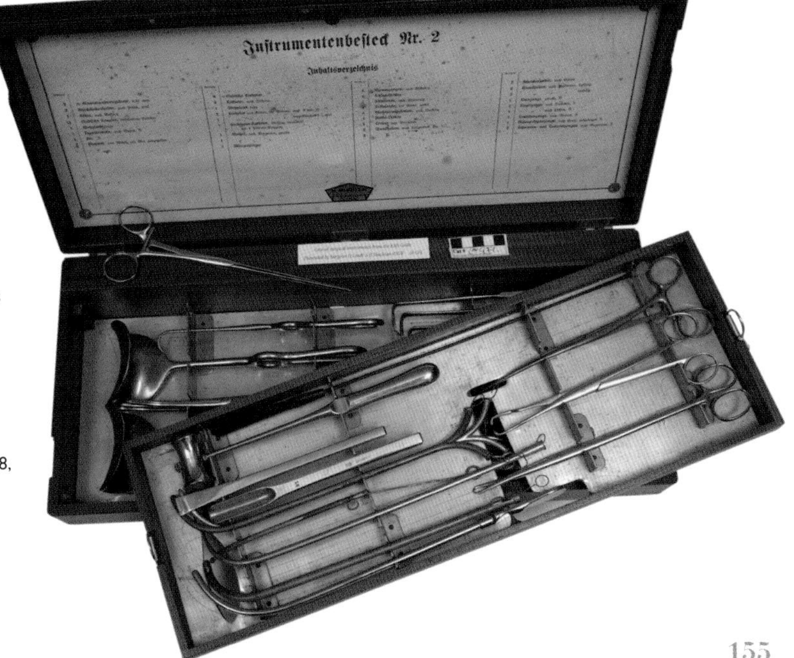

Surgical Instruments from Hitler's yacht KMS Grille.
The KMS Grille was presented to Hitler by the German nation as a private yacht, but designed for easy conversion to a fast mine layer. She was brought to Rosyth, near Edinburgh, as a 'prize of war.' The ship had a well equipped sick bay with operating theatre and X-ray room. RCSEd Collections.

Skull from the Battle of the Pyramids, July 1798, showing sabre cuts. BC xvii.6 GC 11138. Photo Max McKenzie.

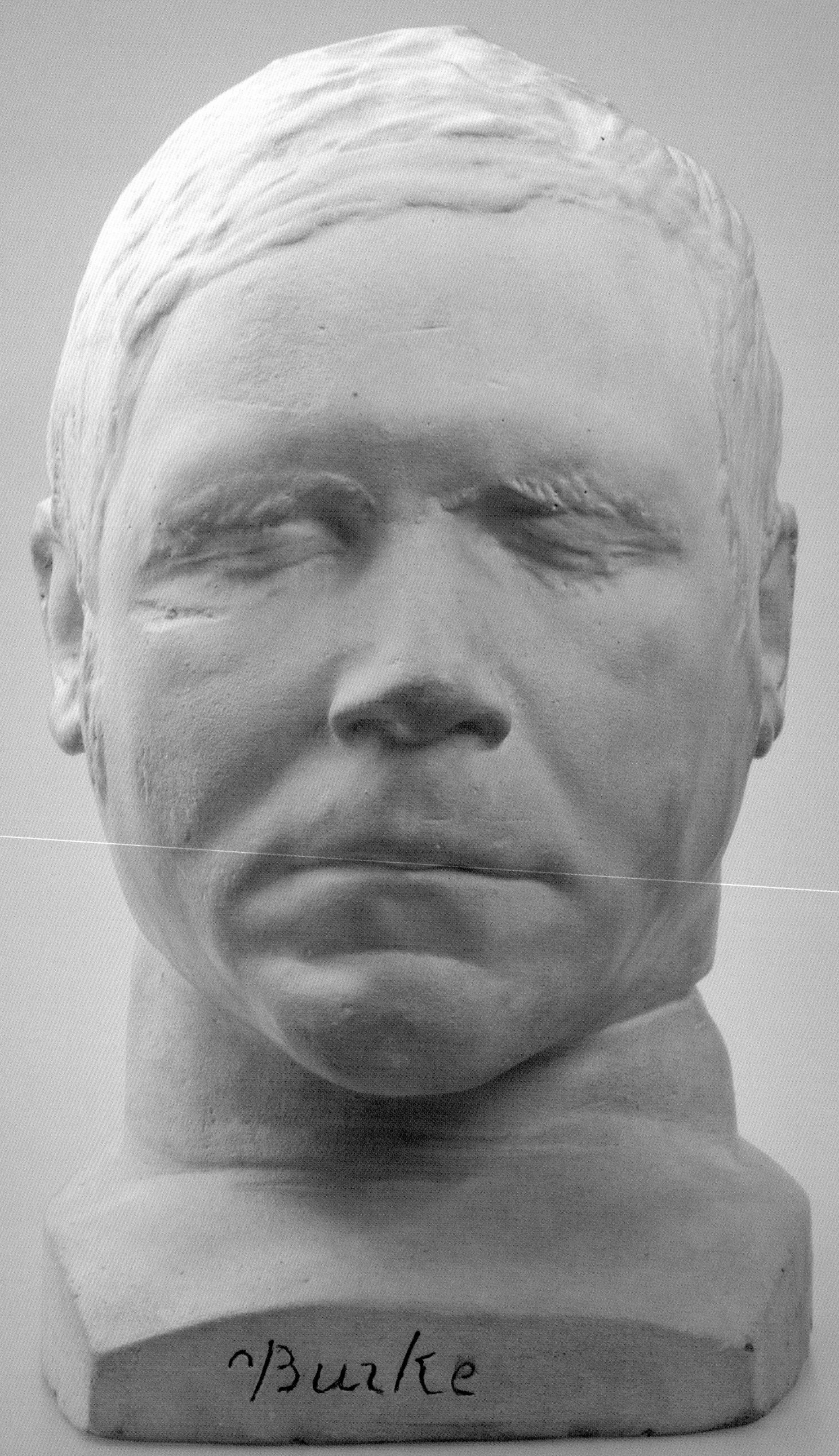
Burke

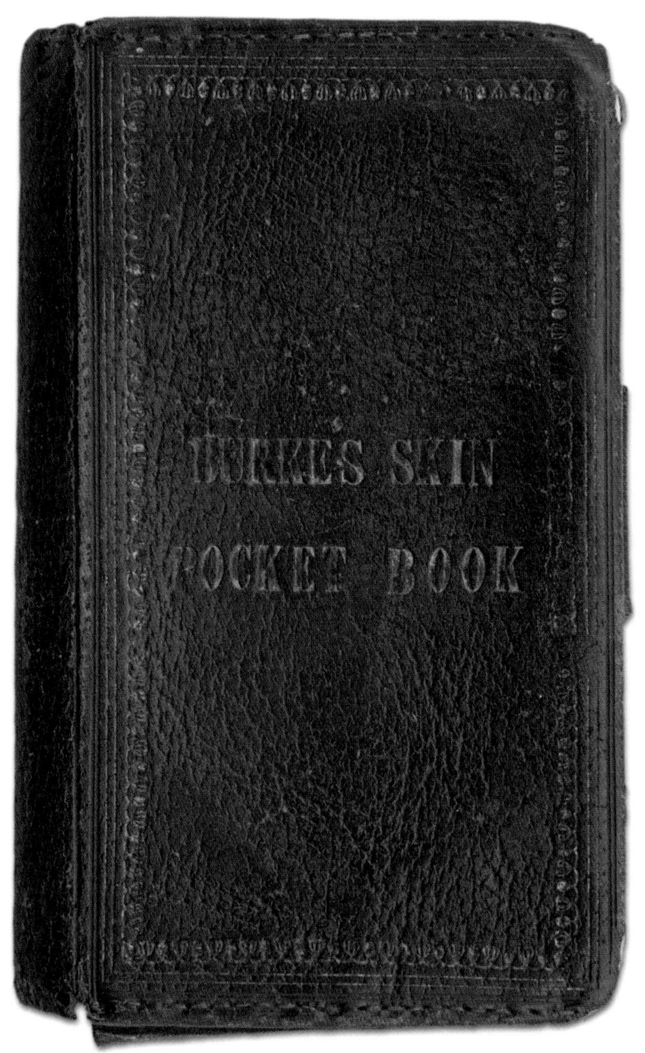

▲ **Pocket-book reputedly made from the skin of William Burke** after his corpse had been publicly dissected by Professor Alexander Monro *tertius*. RCSEd Collections.

◀ **Plaster cast of William Burke's head** made immediately after his execution, 28 January 1829. RCSEd Collections.

Robert Liston

Robert Liston (1794-1847) became a Fellow of RCSEd in 1818; famed for his speed, dexterity and strength in amputations, he was considered the finest technical surgeon of his day.

He presented a set of his surgical knives to the College on the opening of Surgeons' Hall in 1832. In 1834 he moved to London and in 1846 undertook the first major operation in Britain while the patient was under ether anaesthetic, successfully amputating the patient's leg in 28 seconds.

'The more rapidly, consistently with safety, these operations be accomplished, the better.'
ROBERT LISTON

Robert Liston (1794-1847) by Clarkson Stanfield (1793-1867), c.1820. RCSEd Collections.

Post operative casts in wax and plaster of a facial tumour removed by Robert Liston in 1834 from a 34 year old woman. GC 1706.

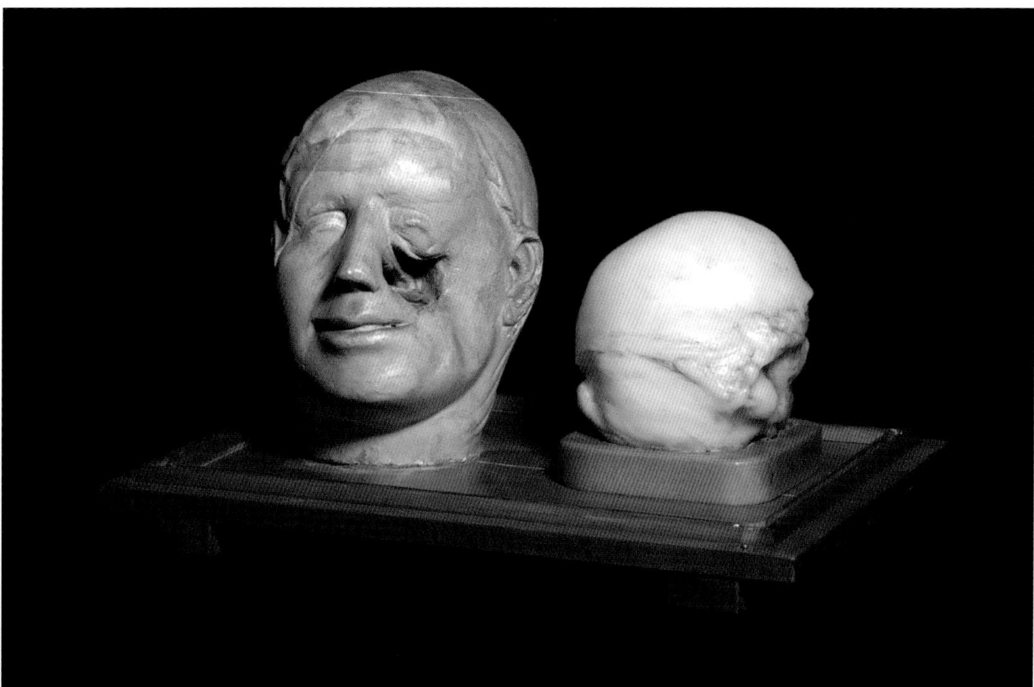

ROBERT LISTON
SEPTEMBER 29TH 1818.

James Syme

◀ **James Syme (1799-1870)** by Sir George Reid (1841-1913). RCSEd Collections.

▶ **Portrait of Robert Penman** aged 24 years showing a massive tumour of the lower jaw which was excised by James Syme in 1828 without anaesthesia. The operation lasted 24 minutes and the blood loss was about 250mls.

▼ **Large fibro-osseous tumour** removed from Robert Penman's lower jaw, 1828. RCSEd Collections.

The Napoleon of Surgery

James Syme (1799-1870), although less flamboyant than his arch rival Robert Liston, was also considered one of the greatest surgeons of his generation.

He became particularly famed for his techniques in the especially difficult amputations at the hip joint and the ankle. A Fellow of the College he was appointed to the Chair of Clinical Surgery at Edinburgh University in 1833. Already a curator of the museum he was to continue as an ex-officio member of the museum committee until 1869, the year before his death.

James Young Simpson

KATHLEEN JAMIE

The way the light falls on Simpson's substantial coat suggests the coat is made of moleskin or velvet. It's a garment that speaks of worldly success, and it's large because James Young Simpson had no small frame. 'A head of Jove and the body of Bacchus' wrote poet Gerald Massey.

This photograph was probably taken in the early 1850's. Simpson was born in 1811, and so was 42 or 43 at that time. He was already famous and successful, but this image still shows something of his early ambition. It's in the way one hand clasps the walking stick and the other the arm of the chair, as if he were just about to rise and get back to work.

He drove himself hard. In a speech to young medical graduates, given when he was Professor of Midwifery, Simpson cautioned against any waste of time. Indeed, he calculated that if a person were to rise every day at 5am, he would add, so to speak, 15 years on to his life. He cautioned the students against the 'self-slavery of indolence.' 'Well or ill', he said once 'I must work.'

The lustrous coat, alas, does not survive among the Simpson collection at RCSEd. (However, things turn up unexpectedly, and RSCEd has received many surprise donations over the years). It was actually made of sealskin; a note taped to the back of the photograph's frame begins, 'This photo of James Young Simpson was taken in his sealskin coat which was presented to him by the ladies of Edinburgh in gratitude for his wonderful discovery...'

Whether or not he required a coat was a moot point – he was by then a wealthy man. He did, however, require pockets. Simpson was famously disorderly. One friend noted that, when Simpson received a message, 'The note was thrust in a capacious pocket, which received and held...many strange epistles.' Even before his 'wonderful

Sir James Young Simpson wearing the sealskin coat presented to him 'by the Ladies of Edinburgh in gratitude for his wonderful discovery of anaesthesia.' Donated by the Church of Scotland.

discovery' patients clamoured for his attention, and friends were trying to take him in hand. For the sake of his reputation, they said, he should adopt more orderly habits. One wrote 'let your arrangements be changed – whenever on leaving a patient…fix a day for again visiting her, enter it at the moment in your visit book, let it be at all times most correctly kept..'

No coat, but the Museum does hold a pair of James Young Simpson's shoe buckles, and a top hat.

Of humble background, the seventh son of a Bathgate baker – there is something both kindly and doughy in both his countenance, and his obstetrician's hands – Simpson seems to have been driven by both compassion and worldly ambition. Several myth-like stories append to Simpson. One, told in J Duns' 1873 Memoir, says that when Simpson was a student he observed a surgical operation but was so aghast at the patient's agony, he fled the operating theatre, renounced medicine and went straight to sign on as a clerk. However, like Dick Whittington he 'turned again' to complete his training and became, at the young age of 28, and not without opposition, Professor of Midwifery at Edinburgh University. Among his obstetric instruments held by RCSEd, are an elegant, ebony foetal stethoscope and forceps of his own design.

▲ **Top hat, quill pen and letter** belonging to James Young Simpson. RCSEd Collections.

By the 1840s, aside from his hospital work, Simpson had built an impressively aristocratic list of private patients. Simpson's brother Alexander was still in the family baking trade, and he had helped Simpson through many financial difficulties in the early days. To him James wrote, perhaps wryly: 'I was at Hamilton Place last week seeing the Marchioness of Douglas ... In November I expect to bring into the world heirs to the Earldoms of W.R,. and M. . I all but agreed to make a visit to Lord and Lady Douglas, to try and shoot grouse!'

However, despite these grand visits, it was Simpson's own house at 52 Queen Street which became the hub of his activities. He had bought the property in 1845, because of his growing practice, and his growing family (Mrs Jessie Simpson, nee Grindlay, bore 9 children, but two died in infancy and two died as young men).

The dining room at Simpson's house, 52 Queen Street, Edinburgh where the first experiments with chloroform took place.

52 Queen Street was therefore the site of Simpson's famous discovery. It was 1847, Simpson's annus mirabilis, and he was 36. In the January he was appointed queen's surgeon in Scotland, but he had other things on his mind. To his brother, Simpson wrote:

'Flattery from the queen is perhaps not common flattery but I am far less interested in it than in having delivered a woman this week without any pain while inhaling sulphuric ether. I can think of naught else.'

Sulphuric ether was by then not uncommon as an anaesthetic in surgical operations. It had been publicly demonstrated in the USA by dentist William Morton, but it was foul smelling and volatile, so on both sides of the Atlantic the race was on in to find a better alternative.

The story – perhaps another of the myths – unfolds one evening in November 1847. After dinner with guests at Queen Street, Simpson produced this brandy decanter containing chloroform. His friends and colleagues were accustomed to experimenting; Simpson wrote that, throughout that spring of 1847, he had 'tried upon myself and others the inhalation of different other volatile fluids.' So when each guest was served a little of this new potion they all knew what to do. All inhaled, and promptly fell to the floor, including a niece, Miss Agnes Petrie, who went down crying 'Oh, I am an angel!'

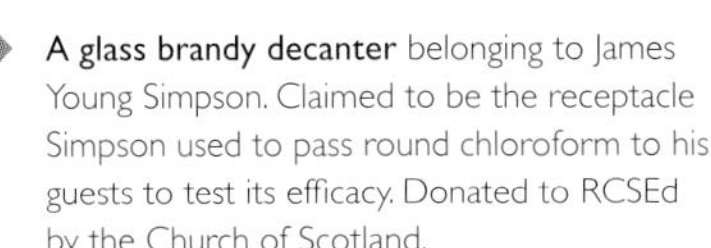

A glass brandy decanter belonging to James Young Simpson. Claimed to be the receptacle Simpson used to pass round chloroform to his guests to test its efficacy. Donated to RCSEd by the Church of Scotland.

Simpson's own letters, however tell a slightly different version.

Chloroform was a chemical which had first been synthesised in 1831, but it seemed such an inauspicious substance that, although he'd had some prepared, Simpson hadn't bothered to try it. Then, as a scrap of a letter in his own hand describes:

'..it seemed so unlikely a liquid to produce results of any kind, that it was laid aside, and on searching for another object among some loose paper, after coming home very late one night, my hand chanced to fall upon it, and I poured some of the fluid into tumblers before my assistants Dr Keith and Dr Duncan and myself. Before sitting down to supper we all inhaled the fluid, and were all "under the mahogany" in a trice to my wife's consternation and alarm. In pursuing the inquiry thus rashly perhaps begun, I became every day more and more convinced of the superior anaesthetic qualities of chloroform as compared with ether.'

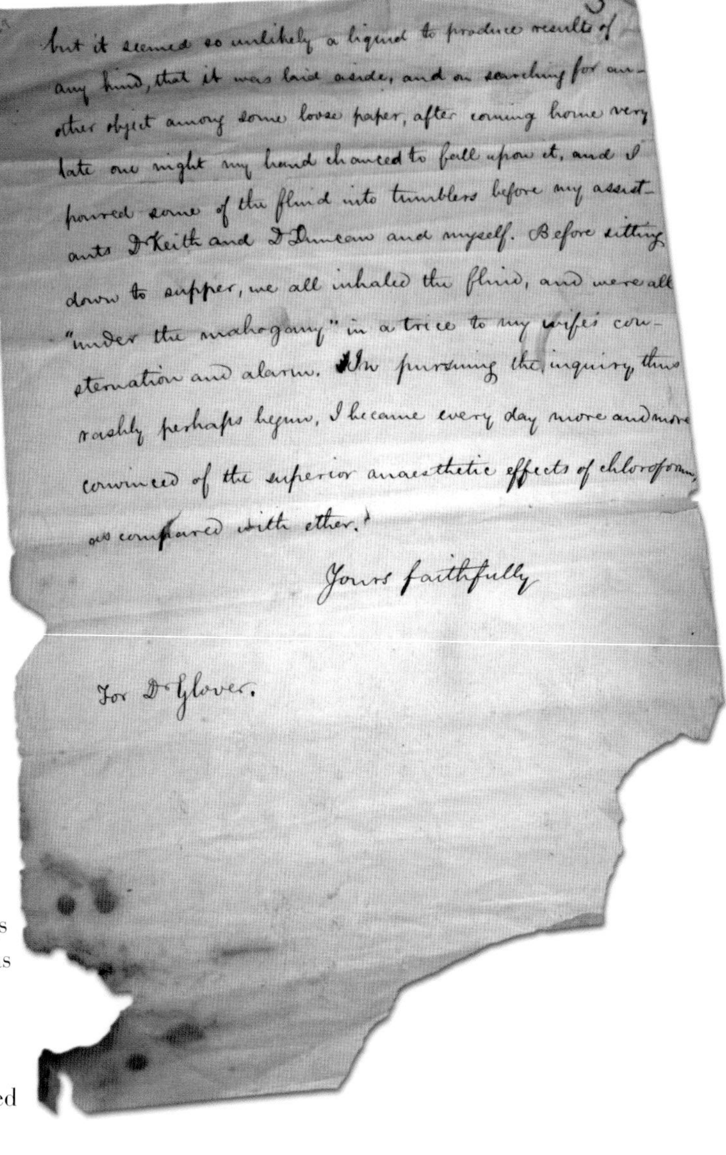

3

but it seemed so unlikely a liquid to produce results of any kind, that it was laid aside, and on searching for another object among some loose paper, after coming home very late one night my hand chanced to fall upon it, and I poured some of the fluid into tumblers before my assistants Dr Keith and Dr Duncan and myself. Before sitting down to supper, we all inhaled the fluid, and were all "under the mahogany" in a trice to my wife's consternation and alarm. In pursuing the inquiry thus rashly perhaps begun, I became every day more and more convinced of the superior anaesthetic effects of chloroform as compared with ether.

Yours faithfully

For Dr Glover.

Given what we know of the chaos of Queen Street, a late night rummage through a pile of papers is eminently believable.

There's no doubt, though, that 'drugs parties' were held. Once discovered as an effective anaesthetic, chloroform had to be refined. In the RSCEd archive is a list, in Simpson's hand, of 13 differently sourced and prepared samples of chloroform, of differing purities, all of which had to be tried, and results compared. Such experimenting was dangerous.

Simpson made himself ill with it, but there was fun too. A letter of condolence from Mrs Elizabeth Tootal to Lady Simpson after her husband's death reads: 'I have never forgotten the days when we were all experimenting together. And laughing together – and crying – in the early days of Chloroform when we were all useful or desired to be so! & happy!'

46

Marlfield House,
Adlington.
nr. Macclesfield

May 10th

My dear Lady Simpson
I do not know how to condole with you, or how to sympathize with you on this dreadful and national bereavement but this I do know. that I do very deeply and sincerely mourn the loss you have sustained – & feel for you & with you in your great grief – Dear good Great Dr Simpson – so simple minded & so lofty! All at once – truly we shall never never

Whatever the precise circumstances, this much is clear: Simpson's pamphlet, 'Discovery of a New Anaesthetic Agent', was published on 10th November. By the close of 1847 the substitution of chloroform for ether had likewise been made 'in a trice.' Within weeks chloroform was being used in surgery and childbirth, and Simpson was receiving congratulations on his discovery from doctors and patients throughout Europe. Gifts came too, like the sealskin coat, and honours and awards. In 1849 he was President of the Royal College of Physicians. A Baronetcy followed in 1866.

There were, however, religious objections to anaesthesia, as there had been to inoculation one hundred years before. Simpson was never one to sidestep controversy and immediately began publishing against the objectors. He could use reasoned and theological argument in print, but his personal reaction was more visceral. Upon learning that one such objector was to address a meeting in Edinburgh, Simpson wrote 'I have a great itching to run up and pound him.'

When Queen Victoria herself used chloroform during childbirth in 1853, its public acceptance was guaranteed. Chloroform had its drawbacks, though, and reports soon were heard of patients dying, allegedly under its influence.

The search for better anaesthetic agents went on. But as for James Young Simpson, in the words of his biographer Dun, he enjoyed 'complete success.'

Although Simpson by then had staff and assistance, and a country house to which his family could retreat, he conducted clinics at Queen Street, attending many kinds of cases, not only obstetric. Things were still chaotic. A vivid description survives, written in 1852 by an American visitor, Dr Channing of Boston:

'When he began this system of home clinics…his house was filled at all hours, so that it was impossible to keep any order. People would come at 7am, in order to be first… I am surprised again at the varieties of disease which congregate at No 52...'

Pill Box belonging to James Young Simpson. RCSEd Collections.

Perhaps from this time dates this tin pill-box. The lid opens to reveal 11 little compartments. These are marked variously Lead and Opium pills. Blue Pills, Pil Croton, Pil Doveri, Suppos. morph. These are analgesics and purgatives, mostly. The pills are still inside; little hand rolled pellets, or powders within neat folds of paper.

At Queen Street, a ticketing system was devised, clinic hours were set from half past one to half past five, and two large rooms given over to house the waiting patients. Dr Channing goes on:

'Here are the poor and the rich together. And I can say, from a long and wide observation that there is no difference in their treatment...' After swift diagnosis 'he proceeds at once to the treatment. If an operation is to be, he does it at once. Applications of remedies are made, and prescriptions given...His meals are often interrupted. His butler brings in cards, notes, letters.

Then two or three ladies come in. Then gentlemen, with or without ladies…his house is very large and full of rooms, and always seems inhabited.'

There was also the night-bell. The household, in the words of Simpson's nephew 'was accustomed to the midnight ring.'

Simpson seemed a man of apparently boundless energy. As well as obstetrics, he wrote letters, and published papers, on medical subjects as diverse as pathology, homeopathy (which he refuted), hermaphroditism, and leprosy.

Daguerrotype of James Young Simpson c 1850. Daguerrotypes are a method of photography by mercury vapour development of silver iodide exposed on a copper plate.

There were other interests too. Archaeology and antiquarianism had been favourite pursuits since boyhood. Near his native Bathgate, (and now within a stone's throw of the runway of Edinburgh airport) is the Cat Stane. This megalith, with a Roman inscription, was an object of particular fascination.

In 1862 Simpson published a paper on it. As well as a pre-eminent doctor, he was by then Honorary Professor of Antiquities to the Royal Scottish Academy. RCSEd holds many letters and papers pertaining to this archaeological interest. There are also papers concerning Simpson's increasing interest in Church affairs, and his Christian belief.

Despite his will to work, or perhaps because of it, Sir James Young Simpson died in May 1870, at the relatively young age of 58. He died at his home at Queen Street. His funeral was a phenomenon. 30,000 people lined the streets. The University closed at noon, the stock exchange shut. According to the Scotsman the procession was extraordinary. The general public, the students, the city incorporations, the ecclesiastical and academical courts, and the legal, scientific, literary and artistic societies formed the first part of the procession, then came the 'stately catafalque' and then 'a string of ten mourning coaches and about sixty private carriages with relatives and members of the council behind.' 'The general business of the city was brought to a pause...and altogether there was presented the impressive spectacle of a great community doing a last act of homage to departed genius and worth.'

Lady Simpson outlived her husband by only a few weeks. She did not live to see his statue unveiled in Princes Street Gardens. In time the house at 52 Queen Street, now called Simpson House, was gifted by the Simpson family to the Church of Scotland and is presently run as a drugs and alcohol counselling centre. Until the last days of 2007 the dining room of that house was maintained as a simple museum and homage to James Young Simpson and the discovery of chloroform.

In 2007 the Kirk, under pressure of its own work, could no longer spare the space, and the 'Discovery Room' with its maroon wallpaper and heavy Victorian furniture was reluctantly disbanded. The Simpson memorabilia, – including the famous brandy decanter – was donated to the Museum.

James Young Simpson: If it is our mission ...

GAEL TURNBULL

'If it is our mission
to alleviate suffering
as well as to preserve life
there should be no conscientious restraint

and if God has benevolently given us means
to mitigate the agony
it is His evident intention
that we should employ it

which requires no special kind of instrument –
even the perfume is not unpleasant
with ten to twenty inspirations being enough,
sometimes fewer,
so that sleep speedily follows –

and on one of the first occasions
after the influence had passed off
it was a matter of no small difficulty
to persuade the astonished mother
that the baby presented to her
was her own living child.'

Joseph Lister

Joseph Lister was born in 1827 in London. After qualifying as a doctor he moved to Edinburgh in 1853 to train in surgery under James Syme. He later married Syme's daughter.

In 1860 he was appointed to the Regius Chair of Surgery at Glasgow University and it was there that in August 1865 he performed an operation on an 11 year old boy who had a compound fracture of the left leg. The operation was not dramatic in itself, but the simple dressing of the wound with lint soaked in carbolic acid saved the boy's leg from amputation, often the only course of action in cases where the broken bone had pierced the skin and gangrene was likely to develop. The carbolic acid mixed with the blood and formed a crust over the wound preventing infection and allowing time for the fracture, carefully splinted, to heal. After further dressings with a more diluted solution the boy was able to leave hospital only six weeks later. Lister's reputation grew as a result of this breakthrough which greatly reduced mortality rates for amputation to just fifteen percent, an astonishing success at a time when such operations were often fatal.

The Chief

His brow spreads large and placid, and his eye
Is deep and bright, with steady looks that still.

Soft lines of tranquil thought his face fulfil-
His face at once benign and proud and shy.

If envy scout, if ignorance deny,
His faultless patience, his unyielding will,
Beautiful gentleness, and splendid skill,
Innumerable gratitudes reply.

His wise rare smile is sweet with certainties,
And seems in all his patients to compel
Such love and faith as failure cannot quell.
We hold him for another Herakles,
Battling with custom, prejudice, disease,
At once the son of Zeus with Death and Hell.

W. E HENLEY, poem about Joesph Lister, 1875.

Joseph Lister (1827-1912) by Dorofield Hardy after the original by W. Ouless. RCSEd Collections. Photo Max McKenzie.

The literary editor and poet, William Ernest Henley was 24 and had already had one leg amputated below the knee, due to tuberculosis, when in 1873 Joseph Lister took him on as a patient at the Edinburgh Royal Infirmary. Lister had moved back to Edinburgh in 1869 to become Professor of Clinical Surgery.

It was hoped that Lister could save Henley's other leg, and he did, although Henley remained in hospital for over a year and a half.

Robert Louis Stevenson visited Henley in the Infirmary and the two men became friends and literary collaborators. In 1880 they wrote a play together: *Deacon Brodie or The Double Life*. Brodie's double life was the inspiration for Stevenson's later work *The Strange Case of Dr Jekyll and Mr Hyde*, but it was Henley who inspired another of Stevenson's most lasting characters:

'Henley could not cross a room without his crutch... He was a splendidly ironic, bearded man, and John Silver was Stevenson's idea of Henley taken to piracy. It was Henley's crutch that Silver threw to clinch an argument...'

JM BARRIE
The Greenwood Hat

Carbolic Spray c 1880. The glass cup was filled with a solution of carbolic acid. Steam generated under pressure was passed through the solution producing a spray which was directed around the wound. RCSEd Collections.

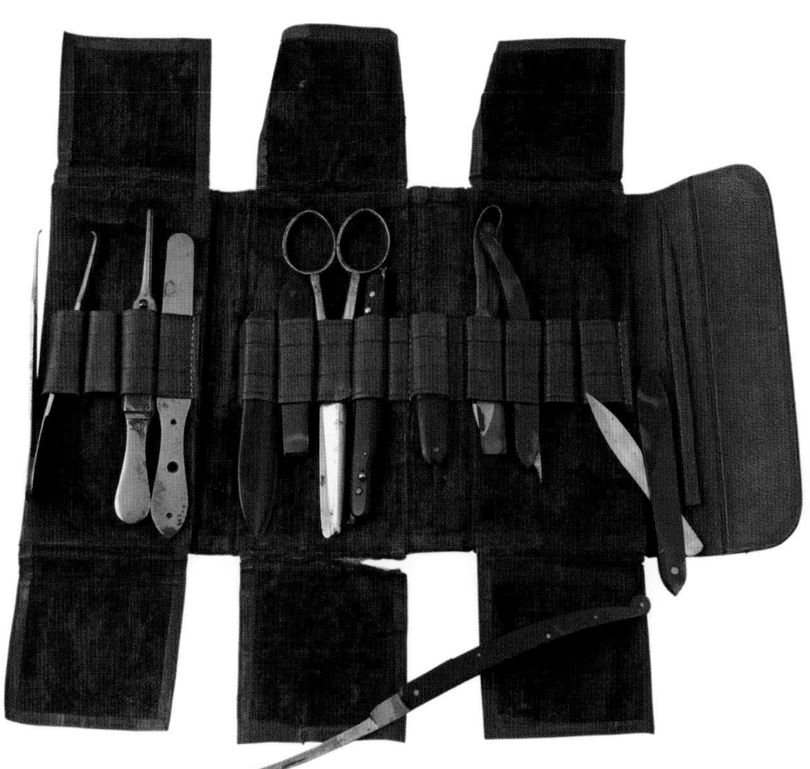

Pocket case of surgical instruments used by Lister in the Royal Infirmary, Edinburgh. HC.AL.1.9.

also a founder member of the Order of Merit.
having earned his eulogy from the Royal
of England, 'His gentle nature, imperturbable
indifference to ridicule and tolerance of hostile
make him one of the noblest of men. His work
humanity will bless him evermore and his fame
although some surgeons such as Spencer Wells and Lawson
Tait obtained excellent results by insisting on absolute clean-
liness at operations they had no real understanding of the cause
of sepsis.
It was Lister who demonstrated beyond doubt the funda-
mental causes of sepsis, and endured ridicule, ostracism and
obstruction of every sort until he won his case. His antiseptic
system was universally accepted and made possible the
development of modern surgery to the immeasurable benefit
of us all.
The seated figure is that of Lister at the height of his fame
and the frock coat is one that actually belonged to him. The
figure holds one of his own drawings of a machine he
designed for the manufacture of carbolic bandages.

The Falls

IAN RANKIN

'He looked around. He was in Hill Square, and there was a sign on the railings nearest to him. Now he knew where he was: at the back of Surgeons' Hall. The anonymous door in front of him was the entrance to something called the Sir Jules Thorn Exhibition of the History of Surgery. He checked his watch against the opening times. He had about ten minutes. What the hell, he thought, pushing the door and going inside.

He found himself in an ordinary tenement stairwell. Climbing one flight brought him to a narrow landing with two doors facing. They looked like they led to private flats, so he climbed a further flight. As he passed the museum threshold an alarm sounded, alerting a member of staff that there was a new visitor.

"Have you been here before?" she asked. He shook his head. "Well, modern-day is upstairs, and just off to the left is the dental display ..." He thanked her and she left him to it. There was no one else around, no one Rebus could see. He lasted half a minute in the dentistry room. It didn't seem to him that the technology had moved so very far in a couple of centuries. The main museum display took up two floors, and was well presented. The exhibits were behind glass, well lit for the most part. He stood in front of an apothecary's shop, then moved to a full-size dummy of the physician Joseph Lister, examining his list of accomplishments, chief among them the introduction of carbolic spray and sterile catgut. A little further along, he came across the case containing the wallet made from Burke's skin. It reminded him of a small leatherbound Bible an uncle had gifted him one childhood birthday. Beside it was a plaster cast of Burke's head – the marks of the hangman's noose still visible – and one of an accomplice, John Brogan, who had helped transport the corpses. While Burke looked peaceful, hair groomed, face at rest, Brogan looked to have suffered torments, the skin pulled back from his lower jaw, skull bulbous and pink.

Next along was a portrait of the anatomist Knox, recipient of the still-warm cadavers.

"Poor Knox," a voice behind him said.'

IAN RANKIN, The Falls, 2001.

Bladed scarificator c. 1825.
In blood-letting the vein was incised by a small, sharp knife called a lancet or fleam. Alternatively, blood could be collected by making multiple, small incisions with a scarificator. This ingenious devise released several sharp blades from a spring loaded, metal container. HC I.3.21.

Trephining drill c. early 1800s.
An early 19th century, hand-operated trephining drill, used to create burr holes in the skull. Power tools would now be used for the same purpose. Although this procedure may seem to be a dramatic modern response to relieve raised intracranial pressure, there is evidence from archaeological remains that prehistoric people also performed such operations. HC I.1.35.

Dry cupping instruments c. 1800.
'Cupping' has been practised for thousands of years for the treatment of disease and pain. Heated cups are placed on the body to encourage blood flow to the surface of the skin. RCSEd Collections.

Squires Inhaler c. 1868.
William Squire was a dentist who helped Robert Liston give the first operation under ether anaesthesia in the UK. Following the operation's success he designed this apparatus. It is the oldest and most complete inhaler of its kind in the world. HC T.1.4.

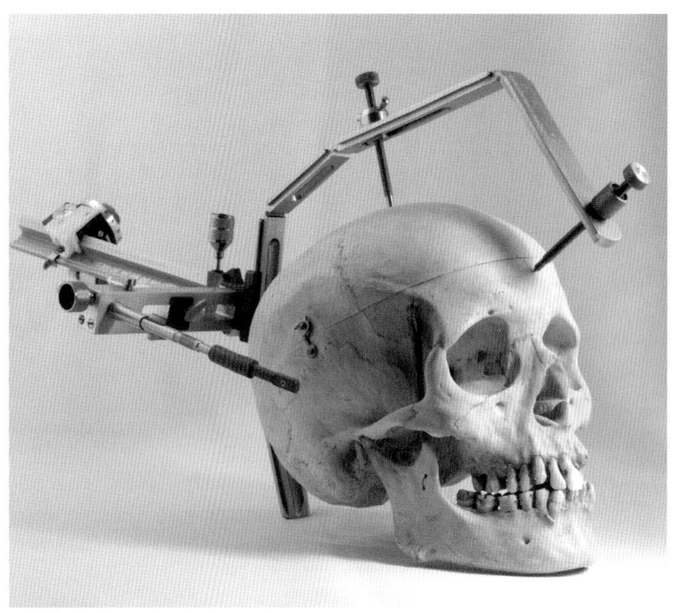

Original stereotactic apparatus for neurological surgery first used in Scotland in 1953 by Professor F J Gillingham. Based on a design by Guiot in Paris and developed over years, it includes a very small motor that slowly drives a microelectrode through the brain. Electrical discharges from grey matter cells are magnified 200,000 times by sound and oscillograph providing precise definition of cerebral nuclei. RCSEd Collections.

Instruments designed by Norman Dott FRCSEd 1930s -1950s.
Clip gun, 'forceps for picking up clips,' two anuerysm needles and two intestinal clamps designed by Prof Norman Dott. Dott was a pioneer of early neurosurgery in Britain. The unassuming looking needles were those used in the first succesful intracranial operation on a cerebral aneurysm, undertaken by Dott in Edinburgh in 1931. RCSEd Collections.

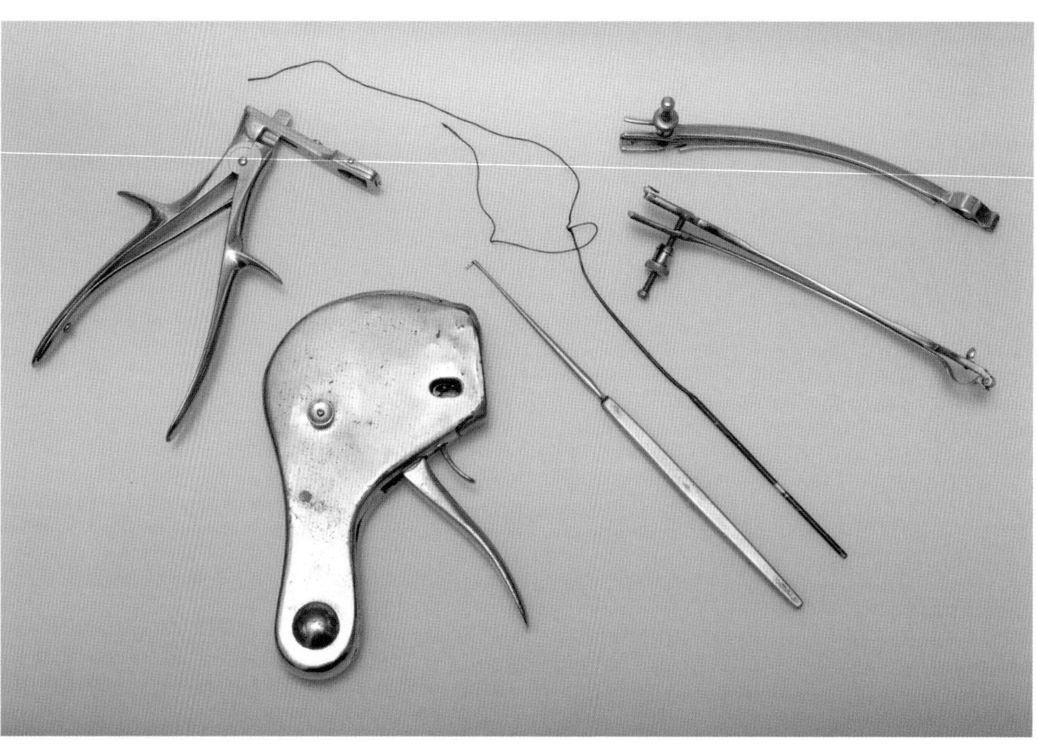

Interventions

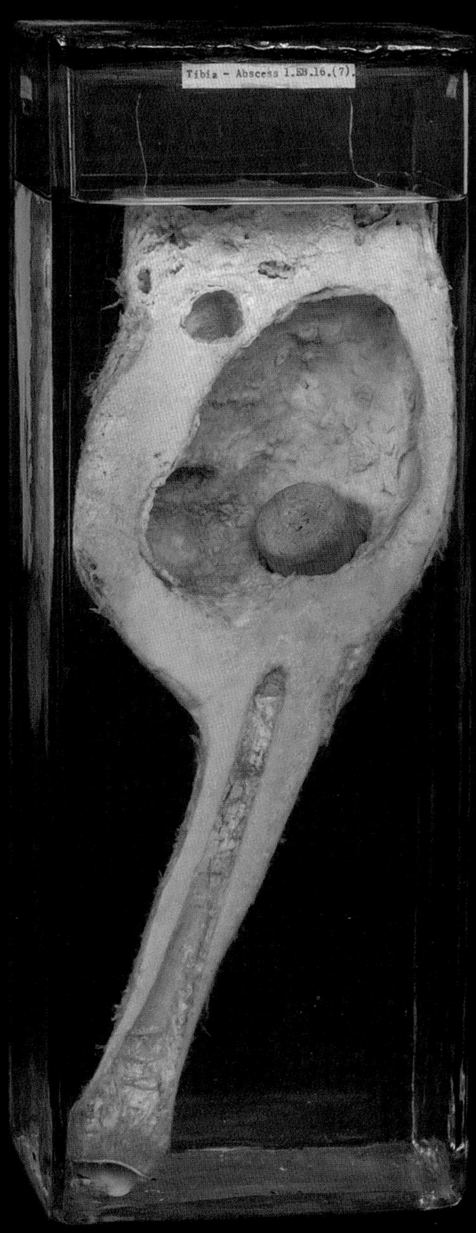

Head of the right tibia, showing a large abscess cavity.

'From a male aged 31 years. When 17 years of age sailing to the Baltic he fell on deck with his leg doubled under him. This man was a sailor on a ship that sailed between Leith and Riga. He had a chronic infection of his tibia which caused great inconvenience and he devised a technique of washing out the sinus/cavity with sea water and then inserted a wooden bung. Over the years the size of the abscess in the bone grew and eventually an amputation was carried out by Dr W Traill of Arbroath in 1831.'
RCSEd Museum Catalogue notes, 1830s. GC 1218.

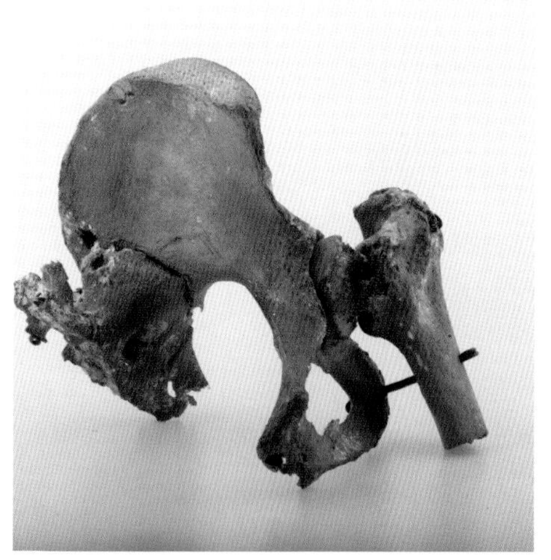

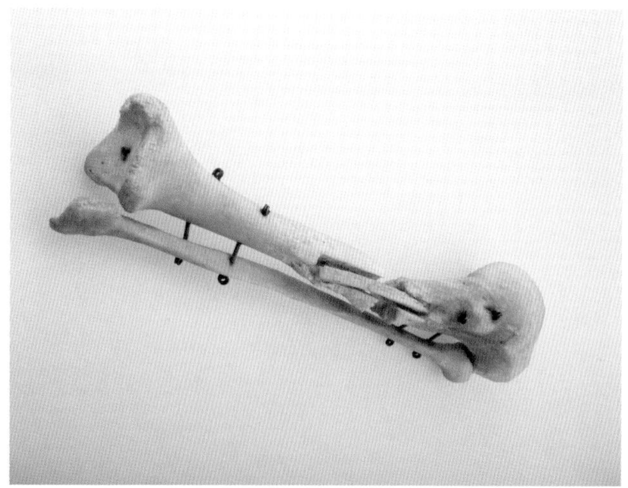

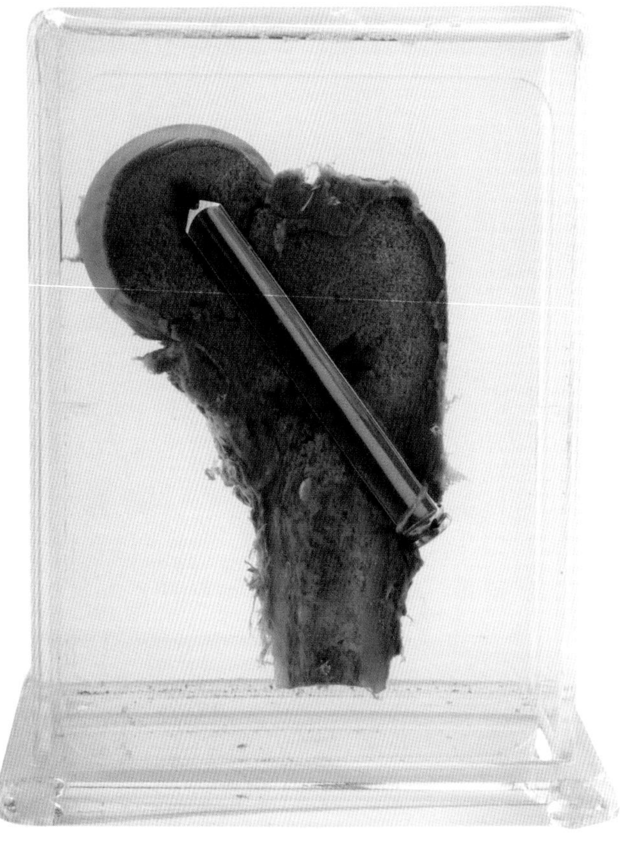

Fracture of the neck of the left femur, 1909. Unsuccessfully treated by the insertion of a metal screw. X-ray control of such operations was not available at the time and the screw completely missed the head of the femur. RCSEd Collections.

Left tibia and fibula (lower leg bones). An un-united fracture of the tibia with autogenous (self generated) bone graft c. mid 20th century. RCSEd Collections.

Smith Petersen's three flanged stainless steel nail. The Smith Petersen nail, first introduced in 1931, was used for fractures of the neck of the femur (thigh bone) and prevented the rotation of the upper fragment of the bone. Stainless steel was recognised as a good inert metal to use in surgical interventions in 1925 as it does not corrode and is strong enough to hold fractured parts of a bone close together until they bond. RCSEd Collections.

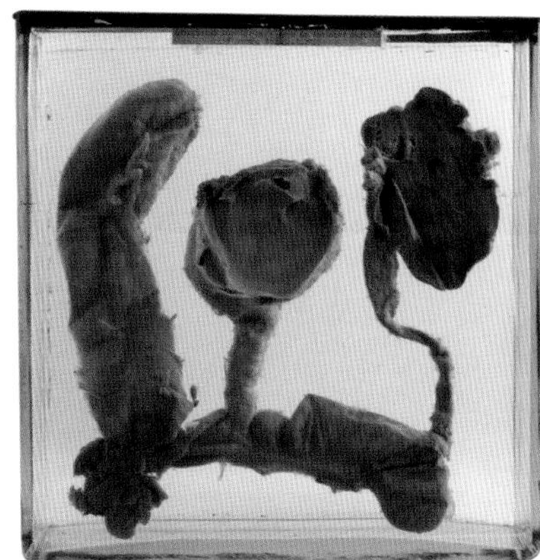

Artificial bladder made from an isolated segment of bowel, into which both ureters were implanted. The operation was performed in the late 1940s and the patient lived for a further six years. Presented by Mr N.J Nicholson, FRCSEd, November 1954. GC 10574.

The first successful vein graft procedure in the UK was carried out by J Hogarth Pringle in 1913. Hogarth Pingle's case notes record that: *'A 49 year old man had noticed a swelling behind his left knee eight months previously and that a double aortic murmer could be heard over his heart. The aneurysm was excised and contained some firm clot. The popliteal artery was divided proximally and a portion of the great saphenous vein was excised and sutured in position to replace the arterial trunk. The man made a good recovery and the grafted vein worked efficiently. The man died three and a half years later of valvular heart disease. Popliteal artery, exised aneurismal sac.'*
GC 7580.

SURGERY
COMES CLEAN
The Life and Work of Joseph Lister (1827-1912)
The development of antisepsis was a landmark in the history of surgery.
This exhibition explains the significance of Joseph Lister's work in the context of Victorian hospital conditions.
Free Admission
6th-31st August 2002
Sir Jules Thorn Exhibition Hall
THE ROYAL COLLEGE of SURGEONS EDINBURGH
50 YEARS OF SURGERY
An exhibition celebrating the 50th Anniversary of the National Health Service
Mon 6th July - Fri 7th August
(weekdays only)
and
Mon 10th August - Sat 5th Sept
(excl. Sundays)
10am - 4pm
THE ROYAL COLLEGE OF SURGEONS OF EDINBURGH
AN EXHIBITION OF
THE HISTORY OF SURGERY
Serratura
THE SIR JULES THORN HISTORICAL MUSEUM
9 HILL SQUARE
OPEN TO THE PUBLIC MONDAY TO FRIDAY WITHOUT CHARGE

Daily opening

The new museum of the History of Surgery opened up opportunities to give the general public greater access to the collections. Dugald Gardner became conservator in 1990 and set out a programme for displays aimed at postgraduate medical students and a series of exhibitions to broaden public understanding of the history of surgery.

◀ **Surgeons' Hall Museum Exhibition Posters.** RCSEd Collections.

▼ The conservator Prof Dugald Gardner and Mr David Wilson (museum technician) watch Mrs Sheena Jones (museum administrator) demonstrate the new laparoscopic training unit donated to the museum by Ethicon PLC. Photo Max McKenzie.

In 1998 a new display in the History of Surgery gallery celebrated the 50th anniversary of the National Health Service. With input from many surgeons prominent in their fields it was well received and brought some important objects into the collections, including early key hole surgery instruments and a laparascopic training unit.

By 1999 the museum was open every week day from 2-4pm, staffed by volunteers, mostly retired College Fellows.

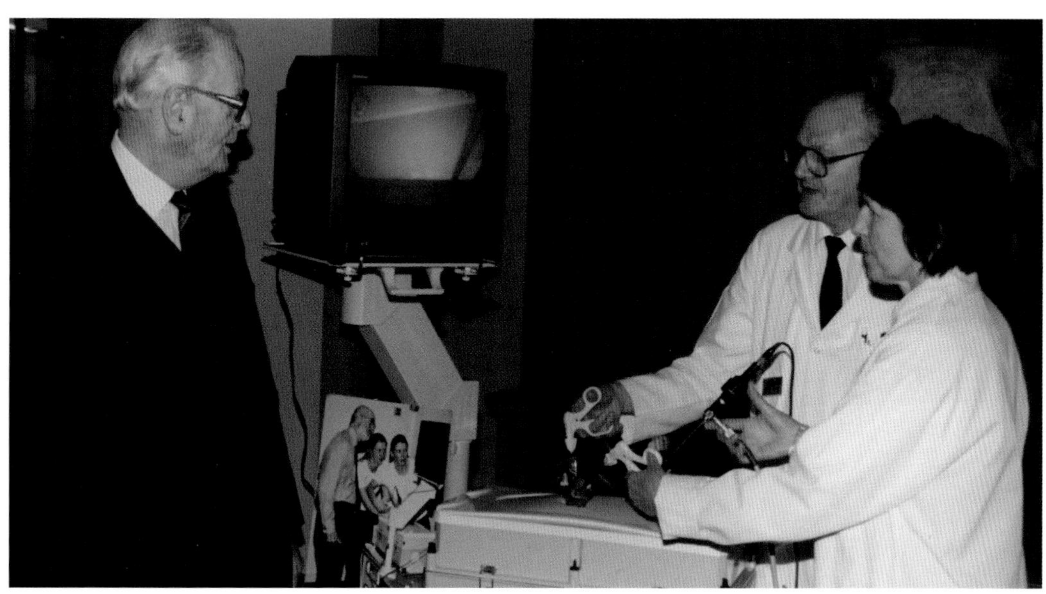

The Museum Today

In 2003 Surgeons' Hall became a fully registered museum and in 2005 the Pathology Museum was opened once again, on a regular basis, to members of the general public.

The museum collections, now listed on an electronic catalogue and accessible online, continue to be enhanced with important donations, purchases and long term loans.

A new public learning programme for school and community groups adds to the growing use of the collections by university and college students, while the Museum also acts as a place of contemplation and inspiration for artists and writers.

Behind the scenes extensive conservation work on the collections continues alongside academic research in medical and non-medical fields, stimulated by new techniques used in tissue analysis and body imaging. Surgeons' Hall Museum has never been so widely used by such a broad range of audiences.

▶ **Andrew Connell**, Surgeons' Hall Museums Collections Manager, 2008.

▼ **Sport, Surgery and Well Being Gallery, Surgeons' Hall, 2009.**

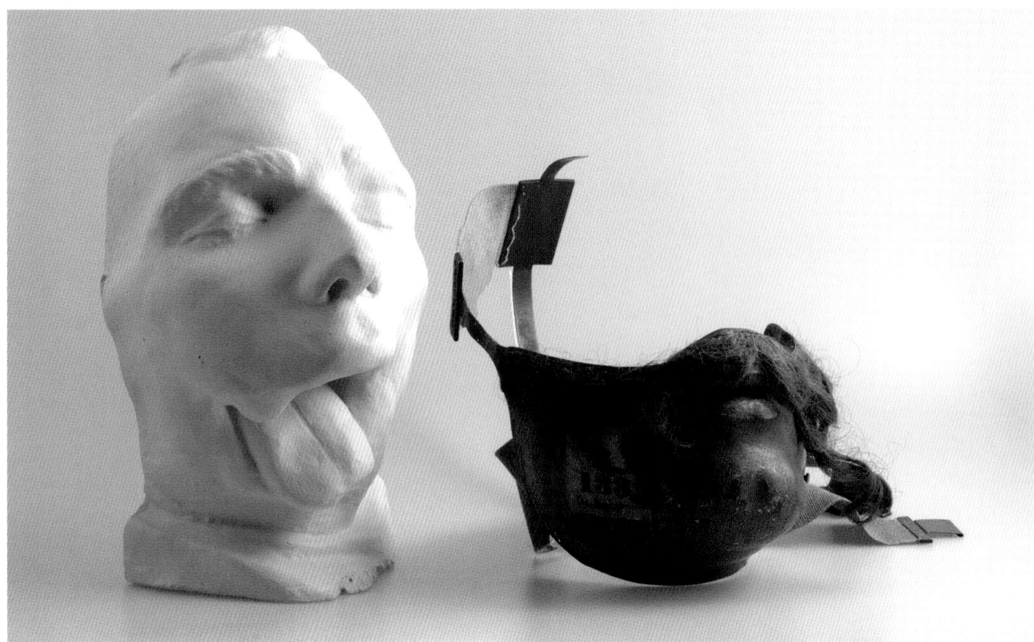

Since the establishment of the new museum of the Royal College of Surgeons of Edinburgh in 1804 some specimens and objects have been disposed of, passed on to other institutions or destroyed – the result of unenviable decisions made when balancing other College priorities, all vying for much needed space or staff or financial resources.

With hindsight, some of the losses can be deeply regretted, such as the loss of much of the Barclay collection and many unique anatomical casts from the 19th century, but the College has, more than any other medical institution in Scotland, saved from destruction and loss many private collections of medical pioneers from the 19th and 20th centuries. It now displays specimens and artefacts from other important collections such as the University of Edinburgh and the National Museums of Scotland.

In 2007 the collection of Surgeons' Hall Museum was one of the first in Scotland to be recognised by the Scottish Government as of National Significance. It is Scotland's largest medical collection, one of the world's great pathology museums and one of the very few open to the general public. It is a rare treasure.

▲ **Cast and contemporary copy of a silver prosthetic mask made in 1833** for Alphonze Louis, a French soldier severely wounded during the siege of Antwerp, December 1832. A mechanism behind the opening for the mouth allowed for eating and drinking whilst being worn. On loan from the University of Edinburgh.

▶ **Surgeons' Hall Pathology Museum, 2008.**

From the Hinterland

ANNA CROWE

This is a world turned inside-out,
a republic of the flesh
both strange and strangely familiar.

The walls are hung with oils,
portraits of common soldiers
who fought at Corunna or Waterloo,
where Charles Bell, army-surgeon,
paints the sun going down in musket-wounds,
with full colours, in a glory
that pale flesh puts on before nightfall.
Below, he adds medical notes, questions
treatment, fumes at his own helplessness.

The tables are ceremoniously laid
with dishes of sprigged china, glass-ware,
entire canteens of polished cutlery:
here are tools for cutting and slicing,
for gripping and probing; even a saw.
But though the cabinets are replete
with choice cuts, the guests
departed years ago.

Some packed up and left, when bodies
grew into homes they couldn't call their own –
unnatural fruit sprouting from floorboards,
timbers shivering into Flemish lace.
As though flesh were determined
to enter the realm of metaphor,
blossoming and hardening
into mineral and vegetable forms
both beautiful and deadly –
one with Crohn's disease leaving
when her bowel became a draper's shop,
stuffed to the gills with pleated, peach-coloured satin;
others retreating as from a volcano
when X-rayed lungs threw up
carcinomas bright as agates;
when skin began to boil, to erupt
in melanomas black as basalt.

Still others groaned with the knowledge
of kidneys turned stone-quarries, sweating
to produce calculi of the finest limestone
and, now and then, a staghorn –
a rough, encrusted twelve-point antler;
a collector's item, having the shape
of the renal pelvic calyceal system.
We use lasers now to shatter kidney-stones,
but fragments may still clump in the ureter,
forming a *steinstrasse* – a cobbled street –
down which the surgeon ventures,
retrieving bits with a mere 'basket.'
Perhaps these ordinary names subdue
some ancient fear of having crossed
a threshold into forbidden places.

Little by little, the body gives up its secrets,
speaks back to us: is it an accident
the structure of the renal pelvis resembles
a calyx, that inner forms, as though to hint
at ancient kinship, should call up
the ghostly presences of plants?
Our nervous system branching, fanning out,
is sheathed like fennel, fine as asparagus-fern;
arteries, veins, capillaries ramifying
like algae, like rosy nets of *corallina*
left by the tide. Morphologies of flow,
like the child's plait the Amazon makes,
seen from the moon, map our dependence
on the laws of life; our kinship real,
in our shared need for water, air and light.

And who can doubt that water was once our home,
seeing these skeletons of foetal hands,
these minute brown transparent bones
poised in jars of formalin?
Delicate as the bodies of insects,
articulated like marine crustacea,
these are travellers from the hinterland
whose journey ended even before it began.
Fish-bones, writing their brief histories
in runes, in ogam-script the colour of blood;
whose perfect, counted fingers
make my own eyes swim with salt.

Professors, Keepers, Conservators, Curators:

Professors

In 1804 the laws for the museum established that five members would be elected annually who with the President and the Professor of Surgery of the Royal College of Surgeons of Edinburgh would form the museum management committee. The Professor of Surgery would manage the museum. The members of the committee were called curators.

1804 – 1821
John Thomson
(1765-1846)

1807 – 1809
James Wardrop
(Assistant)
(1782-1869)

In 1814 the Museum Laws were revised and it was decided that the Professor of Clinical Surgery, if he was a member of the College, be on the museum committee. It was also decided that the post of Keeper of the Museum be created, to be responsible for 'the things contained in it and for the money appropriated for its use.'

Keepers

1816-1821
John William Turner
(d. 1835/6)

1823-1826
Alexander Watson
(later Watson Weymss)
(1799-1879)

Conservators

In 1825 Robert Knox became the Conservator of the anatomy collection he had created at Surgeons' Hall. In 1826 the new post of Conservator of the Pathology Museum was created and this was merged in 1828 with the conservatorship of the Barclay Collection.

1826 -1831
Robert Knox
(1791-1862)

1831-1841
William MacGillivray
(1796-1852)

1841-1843
John Goodsir
(1814-1867)

1843 -1845
Henry (Harry) Goodsir
(c.1815-c.1848)

1845
Archibald Goodsir

1845-1852
Hamlin Lee

1853- 1869
William Rutherford Sanders
(1828-1881)

1869 *interim*
Douglas Argyll Robertson
(1837-1909)

1869/70-1875
James Bell Pettigrew
(1834-1908)

1875-1887
Robert James Blair Cunynghame
(1840/1-1903)

1887-1900
Charles Walker Cathcart
(1853-1932)

1900-1902
Theodore Shennan
(1869-1948)

1903 Feb – Oct
David Waterston
(1871-1942)

1903-1920
Henry Wade
(1876-1955)

1914-1919 *interim*
Frank Jardine
(1886-1956)

1921-1936
David Middleton Greig
(1864-1936)

1936-1939
Charles Frederic William Illingworth (1899-1991)

1939-1947
John William Struthers (also RCSEd Treasurer, & Secretary and President)(1823-1899)

1947-1955
James Norman Jackson Hartley (1889-1966)

1955 -1974
David Eric Cameron Mekie (1902-1989)

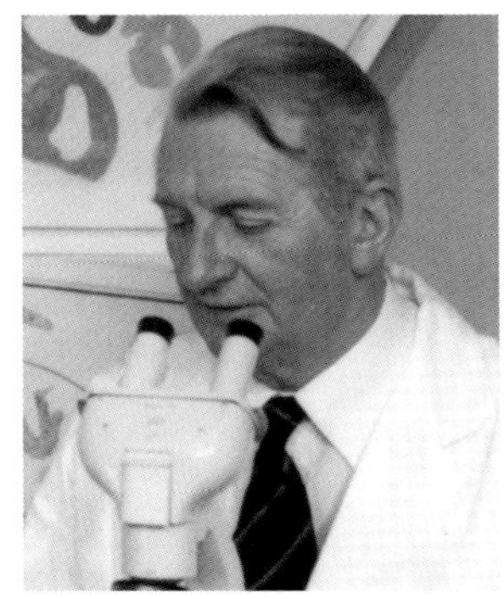

1974 -1984
Andrew Shivas (1922-1996)

1984 -1990
Ian Kirkland (1919-1993)

1990-2002
Dugald Gardner (1924-)

Curator
Director of Heritage

In 2002 the post of Heritage Building Manager/Curator of the Royal College of Surgeons of Edinburgh was created. In 2003 this post was renamed the Director of Heritage.

2002-2009
Dawn Kemp (1961-)

Selected Bibliography & Further Reading

Bell, C., *Letters of Sir Charles Bell selected from his correspondence with his brother George Joseph Bell*, London: John Murray, 1870.

Bridie, J., *The Anatomist* (1930), London: Constable and Co., 1931.

Chalmers, J., *Audubon in Edinburgh. The Scottish Associates of John James Audubon*, Edinburgh: National Museums of Scotland, 2003.

Conan Doyle, A., *Round the Red Lamp, Being Facts and Fancies of Medical Life*, London: Smith, Elder and Co., 1915.

Conan Doyle, A., *A Study in Scarlet in Beeton's Christmas Annual*, London: Ward, Lock and Co.,1887.

Conn, S. (ed), *The Hand that Sees. Poems for the Quincentenary of the Royal College of Surgeons of Edinburgh*, Edinburgh: The Royal College of Surgeons of Edinburgh, 2005.

Creswell, C.H., *The Royal College of Surgeons of Edinburgh. Historical Notes from 1505 to 1905*, Edinburgh: Oliver and Boyd, 1926.

Crumplin, M.K.H. and Starling, P., *A Surgical Artist at War. The Paintings and Sketches of Sir Charles Bell 1809 – 1815*, Edinburgh: The Royal College of Surgeons of Edinburgh, 2005.

Defoe, D., *A tour thro' the whole island of Great Britain, divided into circuits or journies*, (1724-27), Vol. 3, London: J.M. Dent and Co., 1927.

Dingwall, H., *A Famous and Flourishing Society: The History of the Royal College of Surgeons of Edinburgh*, Edinburgh: Edinburgh University Press, 2005.

Gairdner, J., *Historical Sketch of the Royal College of Surgeons of Edinburgh*, Edinburgh: Sutherland and Knox, 1860.

Gardner, D., *Surgeon, Scientist, Soldier. The Life and Times of Henry Wade 1876-1955*, London: Royal Society of Medicine, 2005.

Gordon-Taylor, G. and Walls, E., *Sir Charles Bell. His Life and Times*, Edinburgh: E&S Livingstone, 1958.

Guthrie, D., *The Medical School of Edinburgh*, Edinburgh: George Waterston and Sons, 1959.

Hartley, J.N.J., *The Early History of the Museum of The Royal College of Surgeons of Edinburgh*, Edinburgh Medical Journal Vol. LV No9, Oliver and Boyd, Edinburgh, 1948.

Henley, W.E., *A Book of Verses*, London: David Nutt, 1888.

Jamie, K., *Findings*, London: Sort of Books, 2005.

Journal of the Royal College of Surgeons of Edinburgh, 1965, 11: 'Opening of the Menzies Campbell Collection,' pp 81-83.

Kay, J., *A Series of Original Portraits and Caricature Etchings by the late John Kay, with Biographical Sketches and Illustrative Anecdotes*, Edinburgh: James Paterson, 1837-8.

Kaufman, M.H., *Medical Teaching in Edinburgh during the 18th and 19th centuries*, Edinburgh: Royal College of Surgeons of Edinburgh, 2003.

Kaufman, M.H. *Musket-Ball and Sabre Injuries from the First Half of the Nineteenth Century*, Edinburgh: Royal College of Surgeons of Edinburgh, 2003.

Kaufman, M.H., *John Barclay (1758-1826). Extra-Mural Teacher of Human and Comparative Anatomy in Edinburgh*, Edinburgh: Royal College of Surgeons of Edinburgh, 2007.

Kincaid, A, *The Traveller's Companion Through the City of Edinburgh*, Edinburgh: A. Kincaid, 1794.

Lonsdale, H., *A Sketch of the Life and Writings of Robert Knox the Anatomist. By his Pupil and Colleague*. London: Macmillan & Co., 1870.

MacGillivray, W. *Naturalists Library*, Vol XI, Edinburgh: W.H. Lizars and Stirling and Kenney, 1841.

Macintyre, I. and MacLaren, I. (eds), *Surgeons' Lives. Royal College of Surgeons of Edinburgh. An Anthology of College Fellows over 500 Years*, Edinburgh: The Royal College of Surgeons of Edinburgh, 2005.

Masson, A.H. B., *Portraits, Paintings and Busts in the Royal College of Surgeons of Edinburgh*, Edinburgh: The Royal College of Surgeons of Edinburgh, 1995.

Masson, A.H.B., *A College Miscellany: An Illustrated Catalogue of the Treasured Possessions of the Royal College of Surgeons, Edinburgh*, Edinburgh: The Royal College of Surgeons of Edinburgh, 2001.

Monro, A., *'Life of Dr Ar Monro Sr, in his own handwriting,'* in Erlam, H. D., (1954) 'Alexander Monro, *primus*', University of Edinburgh Journal 17 (2), 77-105.

Morgan, N., *Fleshmarket*, London: Hodder Children's Books, 2003.

MacKail, A. and Kemp, D., *Conan Doyle and Joseph Bell: the Real Sherlock Holmes*, Royal College of Surgeons of Edinburgh: Edinburgh, 2007.

Patrizio, A. and Kemp, D. (eds), *Anatomy Acts: how we come to know ourselves*, Edinburgh: Birlinn, 2006.

Rankin, I., *The Falls*, London: Orion, 2001.

Royal College of Surgeons of Edinburgh College Minutes, 1581 - present.

Rose, D., *Bodywork*, Edinburgh: Luath Press, 2007.

Smith, J. *Catalogue of portraits and busts in the Royal College of Surgeons of Edinburgh*, Edinburgh: Royal College of Surgeons of Edinburgh, 1897.

Stevenson, R.L., *The Bodysnatcher*, in 'Pall Mall Christmas Extra 13,' December 1884.

Stevenson, R.L., *The Strange Case of Dr Jekyll and Mr Hyde*, London: Longmans, Green, 1886.

Szatkowski, S. *Capital Caricatures: A Selection of Etchings by John Kay*. Edinburgh: Birlinn, 2007.

Tansey, V. and Mekie, D.E.C., *The Museum of the Royal College of Surgeons of Edinburgh*, Edinburgh: The Royal College of Surgeons of Edinburgh, 1982.

Thomas, D. *The Doctor and the Devils, and Other Scripts*, New York: New Directions, 1966.

A.Thompson, 'Biographical Account of the late William MacGillivray,' *Edinburgh New Philosophical Journal* (1853), 54: 189-206.

Vertue, G., *Vertue note books [The Note books of George Vertue relating to artists and collections in England]*, Vol. 2, Oxford: The Walpole Society, 1930-1947.

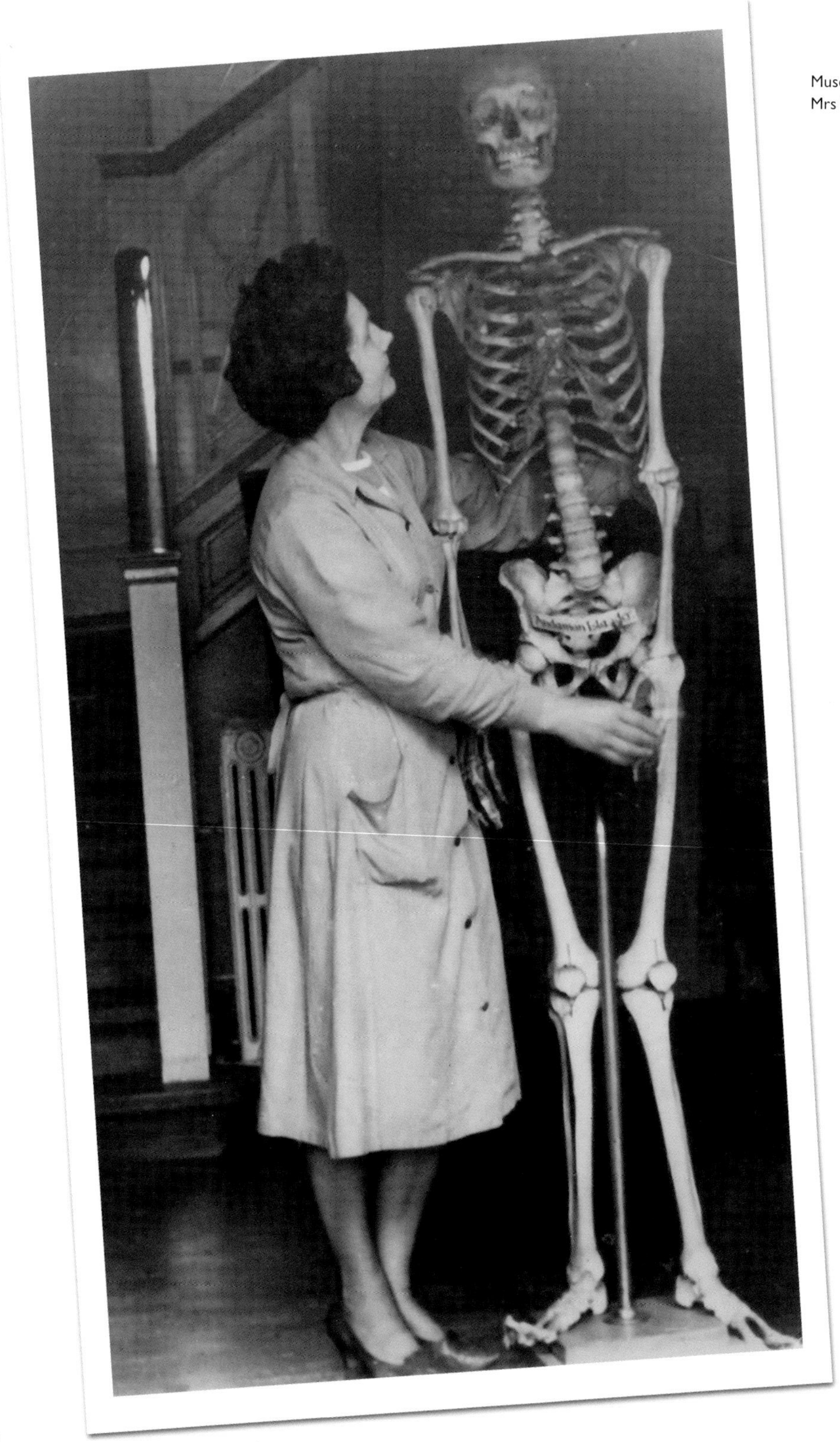

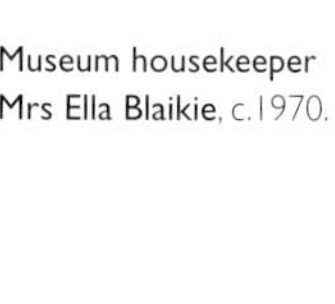

Museum housekeeper
Mrs Ella Blaikie, c.1970.

Acknowledgements

Our immense gratitude to the staff of the Museum and Library of the Royal College of Surgeons of Edinburgh: Emma Black, Andrew Connell, Marion Connell, Thomas Elliott, Steven Kerr, Malcolm MacCallum, Andrew Morgan and Marianne Smith for tirelessly and with good humour helping to provide so much of the material for this book. Whether reviewing the collections in store, preparing specimens and objects for photographing, searching catalogues and records, or covering other duties when all hands were to the deck, it has been a great team effort.

Very special thanks to Ewen Griffiths, Craig McIntyre, marc marnie, Andrew Connell, Kathleen Jamie and the brilliant Elizabeth George for adding their specific creative skills to the project, always with generosity and patience.

Special thanks also to: Max McKenzie, the official staff photographer for Surgeons' Hall for over 30 years, whose work is represented throughout this book and to the Museum volunteers, many of whom have made great contributions to medicine and surgery in Scotland in their own right: David Bremner, John Chalmers, Dorothy Child, Bill Copland, Margaret Cumming, Brian Dale, Ivor Davie, Brian Dean, Dugald Gardner, Enid Gardner, Paul Geissler, George Gordon, Douglas Harper, Phillip Harris, Janet Hayes, Mike Henderson, Lynsey Hutchinson, Christopher Johnston, Allan Mackaill, Ron Macintosh, Iain Maclaren, Bill MacRae, Nigel Malcolm-Smith, Vaughan Martin, Iain McLeod, Geoffrey Millar, Yvonne Mills, Jimmy Scott, Maxwell Shardow, John Shaw, Christine Short, Brian Slawson, Alan Smith, Wilma Steedman, Helen Stewart, Leslie Stokoe, Evelyn Walker and Tony Watson.

For help, support and advice our grateful thanks to: Mark Baillie, Rosie Baillie, Mrs Isabella Blaikie, Helen Dingwall, Liz Hallam, Jess Kemp, Elizabeth Kingdom, Alistair Masson, Iain Macintyre, John Orr, Kenny Ryan, Sheila Szatkowski, Thomas Schnalke, Mike Taylor (Museums Galleries Scotland), Allan Wood, Navena Widulin and Vaughan Yates.

For giving permission to use their work we would like to thank: Elizabeth Burns, John Burnside, Allan Carswell (for his work on Charles Bell), Anna Crowe, Christine de Luca, Valerie Gillies, Edwin Morgan, Ian Rankin, Dilys Rose and Suhayl Saadi and for copyright permissions: The Agency (London) (Lisa Babalis and Nick Quinn), Jenny Brown Associates, Carcanet Press (Pam Heaton), Luath Press (Gavin MacDougall), James Mavor, Jill Turnbull, Orion Publishing (Kate O'Hearn) and the Scottish Poetry Library (Robyn Marsack).

For permissions for non RCSEd images our thanks to: The Arthur Conan Doyle Collection Lancelyn Green Bequest, Portsmouth City Council (Michael Gunton), the Church of Scotland (Glenn Liddell), the National Library of Scotland (Jenny Parkerson), the National Portrait Gallery (Matthew Bailey), the Royal College of Physicians of Edinburgh (Iain Milne), the Royal Commission on the Ancient and Historical Monuments of Scotland (Eleanor Rideout and Kristina Watson), the Royal Scottish Academy (Joanna Soden and Nicola Ireland), the University of Edinburgh (Jill Forrest and John Scally), the University of Aberdeen (Neil Curtis, Martyn Gorman, Alison Hay and Andrew MacGregor) and the White House Historical Association (Hillary Crehan).

To those we have missed our heartfelt apologies our gratitude is no less.

Slide cabinet showing histopathology specimens c. late 19th century. GCM 796.